THE JONES

BALER

STORY

JONES BALERS
ES BALERS
ESMOR WORKS, RHOSESMOR, MOLD.
VAN.
BEDFORD
M 938

THE JONES

BALER

STORY

Gwynfor Williams

Japonica Press

First Published 2011

Copyright © Gwynfor Williams 2011
The moral rights of the author have been
asserted

ISBN: 978-1-904686-23-1

A catalogue record for this book is
available from the British Library

Published by

Japonica Press
Low Green Farm, Hutton, Driffield, East
Yorkshire, United Kingdom, YO25 9PX

Acknowledgements

It has been both a privilege and a pleasure to put together "The Jones Balers Story".

This story could not have been told without the invaluable assistance of so many people.

Most of the information and archive photographs were kindly loaned by three people. These three have also encouraged and helped me in so many ways.

A special thanks to:
Noel Jones the son of Glynne Jones, joint founder and Managing Director of Jones Balers.

John Bumby, personal friend of many years and former Experimental and Test Engineer at Rhosesmor, for all the wonderful stories related to me in Welsh.

Mike Lawrence of Highbridge Somerset, Jones Baler collector and enthusiast.

Between the Allis-Chalmers and Bamfords saga unfortunately all works records seem to have been lost. Without hard facts you must therefore forgive me when I use "estimated" and "probably".

My thanks also to the following:
Robert Archer Garstang, Gareth Beech Welsh Folk Museum, David Brewster IOM. Harold Butler Great Plumpton, Maurice Cragg Conder Green, Martin Cummins, Collinson Garstang, M Downer Mold, Sam Evans Pennal, Stuart Gibbard Moulton Chapel Greenfield Valley Trust, David Hughes Halkyn, David Jones Holywell, Gareth Jones Clawddnewydd, Glyn Jones Denbigh, Mrs JM Jones Gorsedd Holywell, Merfyn Jones Corwen, Dylan Jones Bryn SM, Tudor Jones Chairman Summer Football League, Richard Lancaster Wrea Green, Bill Lister Norfolk, Mold Library, Orry Mitchell IOM, Museum of English Rural Life Reading, Emyr Owen Anglesey, Emrys Owen Llansannan, Jim Perkins ex Petters, Keith Sandwells Johnstown, John Starsmore Wicken, Jo Roberts Llanrwst. Harry Williams Cilcain.

To Mrs Julie Singleton for proof reading and making up for my lack of computer skills.

Last but not least I express sincere thanks to my publisher Stephen Moate and staff at Japonica Press for their support and encouragement.

Author

Gwynfor Williams was born during the Second World War on a farm in Pwllglas near Ruthin, North Wales.

Gwynfor's great grandfather and uncle ran a threshing contracting business dating back to the 1880's, so machinery was "in the blood". Gwynfor's father being a progressive farmer meant that the small mixed farm on which he grew up was a hive of machinery. There were three stationary engines, barn machinery, a Ferguson tractor and a host of field implements. Gwynfor regarded de-cokes, valve grinding and cleaning magneto points as a part of life.

However on leaving school Gwynfor went to Bangor Normal College and became a Qualified Teacher taking up a teaching post in Mold near to the Broncoed Works of Jones Balers.

After eighteen months Gwynfor left to enrol at the Welsh College of Horticulture at Northop, Flintshire, as a student on the then City and Guilds 260 Agricultural Mechanics course led by the late Cecil Jones. The Workshop Technician was John Bumby ex Jones Balers. A lifelong friendship was struck up and Gwynfor started to absorb the experiences of John at Jones Balers.

On completing the City and Guilds course Gwynfor took over the post of Technician vacated by John who moved to be Head of Machinery at Glynllifon College in Caernarfonshire.

1969 saw Gwynfor move to be a lecturer at the then Lancashire College of Agriculture (now Myerscough College) from where he retired in 2003.

Gwynfor is an Honorary Member of the Association of Lecturers in Agricultural Machinery having organized several overseas visits. He is also a founder member of the North Wales Agricultural Machinery Preservation Society and is regarded as the authority on Welsh agricultural machinery.

His other interests include walking and what else would a Welshman do but sing in a couple of choirs.

The Morecambe and Lancaster Welsh Society is also dear to his heart and he seems not to be able to be voted off the committee.

Following one of his illustrated talks he was approached by Noel Jones (son of Glynne Jones of Jones Balers) with the view of writing "The Jones Balers Story". With no works records available to verify facts Gwynfor felt it rather a difficult task. He says that he is far more comfortable with a spanner in his hand than sitting at the computer keyboard.

Having said that starting in 2008 the journey has been most enjoyable and Gwynfor is very grateful for the enthusiasm and support received and trusts that the book is a worthy tribute to the men and women that made Jones Balers.

Contents

Foreword

By Hazel and Noel Jones

For almost twenty years Jones Balers was our life, starting in the darkest days of the Second World War, enduring rationing and hardship. Recognition and success was to follow with the sale of the company in 1961.

Glynne and David Jones earned a worldwide reputation for innovation in baling machines. This is again acknowledged by enthusiasts and our book titled "The Jones Balers Story".

We dedicate this book to all the men and women employed at Rhosesmor and Mold.

Hazel and Noel Jones, wife and son of Glynne Jones, joint founder and Managing Director.

Preface

Many excellent articles on "Jones Balers" have been written, I however felt that there lay a wealth of material and un-told stories that merited an attempt at a book.

The Jones brothers rose from farm labourers to manufacture balers that became the first choice of contractors and farmers from Britain to Australia.

Jones Balers, the name has that lovely Welsh sound to it and combined with the Red Dragon of Wales logo on each machine gave Jones that uniqueness.

The character of the company is a reflection of the Jones brothers. They were enthusiastic sportsmen in footballing and clay pigeon shooting circles; thus the company was keenly competitive and never shied away from taking on the opposition, especially the large American companies of International Harvester and New Holland.

In the world of baler makers Jones became the little company with a big reputation and claimed to manufacture the world's widest range of balers.

Most companies become successful by making the right product at the right time and Jones is no exception. In 1942 there was hardly anything new about their Stationary Baling Presses but the market was crying out for well built reliable machines. Their experience as threshing contractors using presses from other manufacturers meant they had a wealth of experience when it came to building their own. Most of their early products were sold to contractors where speed of work, reliability and service far outweighed the purchase price. The Jones Service was legendary and the "Spares Department" at Rhosesmor had an "open at all hours" operation.

Jones hardly invented new machines but noted the weaknesses of their competitors offerings. Most of the competition was of American origin, their machines often not entirely suitable for British conditions. Jones also filed several clever patents, the famous "Jones Grooved Bale" is probably most remembered.

I have also tried to shed some light on the uniqueness of "The Jones Patented Tucker Knotter" and the World's First Self Propelled Pick-up Baler. Their 'Star' and 'Super Star' balers introduced in 1960 were their finest ever.

It has not been easy to follow "The Jones Balers Story" through the subsequent Allis-Chalmers, Bamford, Bamford International and Benson Group takeovers.

The Jones Dragon breathes again due to the efforts and foresight of an increasing number of Jones Balers enthusiasts.

Chapter 1

FROM FARM LABOURERS TO BALER MANUFACTURERS

OPPOSITE: Glynne Jones co-founder of Jones Balers

Family History of the Jones Brothers

Glyn and David Thomas Jones were from generations of Welsh farming stock. On their fathers side their ancestors can be traced back to the regions of Bala and Corwen. Their great grandfather David Jones in 1825 farmed at Dolywern, Ciltalgarth Cwmtirmynach. Their grandfather Ellis Jones in 1879 farmed Rhydonnen Isaf, Llantysilio near Llangollen. Their father Ellis Jones (Junior) jointly farmed Fron Isa Gwernymynydd Mold. Their mother, a Catherine Jane Jones lived at Trosywern Gwernymynydd, her family hailed from the areas of Betws yn Rhos and Llansannan. By 1907 they had moved to Trefrwd, Nercwys, Mold. It was here in 1908 David Thomas (DT) was born, followed by Jenny in 1910 and Glyn in February 1911. By 1911 the family moved to Tros y Wern, Gwerymynydd

Mold to a farm rented from the Waln's of Fron Hall Gwernymynydd. It was here that three girls were born, Phyllis, Mary and Eluned. In 1926 Ellis, his wife, two boys and four girls were evicted from the farm for non payment of rent. They moved to the Nant, Rhydymwyn, near Mold.

Their holding was too small to support everyone, times were hard and the boys turned their hands to all kinds of farm work on neighbouring farms.

*Agricultural Wages 1925 was £1-11s-6d for a 50 hour week

Their uncle "Teddy" at Aberduna farm ran a steam engine and thresher and David, being the eldest, worked for him in winter. During the summer he drove the steam

TOP: The Jones brothers Glynne and David 1950.

ABOVE: Company Logo (Badge).

RIGHT: Glynne Jones "starting from scratch".

wagon for the nearby Ruby Brick Company at Rhydymwyn. This gave young David experience and an insight into the world of machinery. But ill health was to soon follow and David, like so many, contracted tuberculosis (TB) confining him to over a year at Talgarth Sanatorium near Brecon and Llangwyfan near Denbigh. The journey to Brecon on a motor bike from North Wales to visit his brother in those days must have taken Glyn all day.

Miss Buddicom Pen Bedw, Nannerch of the famous railway engineering family had employed the Jones boys and was impressed with their work installing a water system. This generous lady had perceived that these talented hard working lads deserved success. She offered to advance them a loan to start their own business, this

was duly accepted. It is these chapters in their lives that drew the brothers together and set the seeds that became Jones Balers. The loan was duly paid with interest and several prototype machines were tested at Pen Bedw with Captain Nick Archdale.

1928 Threshing Contractors

David aged 20 and Glyn 17 had between them saved £80 and so started a harvesting contractor's business with a traction engine thresher and binder. Everything was second hand and they quickly learned their skills as engineers. They earned about £10 per week. Every penny beyond personal expenses of 6s a week each they ploughed back into the business. In winter they worked long hours moving from farm to farm by the light

FAR LEFT: At Nant Rhydymwyn 1932 David sister Mary and Glynne.

LEFT: David standing on engine and Glynne with hands in pockets.

BELOW: "Threshing Days" Glynne on the Fowler traction engine.

of hurricane lamps. In summer they took on farm work at 30s a week. Their hard work paid off and they bought their first baler in 1934. The maker was Howard of Bedford. In 1936 a new baler was bought, the "Powell Baling Press" made by Walter Powell of Kirkby near Liverpool, it cost £236. 1937 saw the two brothers probably completing their first major engineering project.

The Howard baler needed a person to feed it, a dangerous dusty job. The Jones brothers adapted it to self feed thus saving the wages and probable health of one person.

David's wife Zillah and young child Merfyn were now residing at Esmor House, Rhosesmor (next to the Post Office). Zillah had beautiful handwriting and was the company secretary. She carried out these duties into the early days of baler building.

In 1937 Glyn Jones married Hazel Eileen Tapley and with their son Noel lived at Berth Ddu a few doors away. Glyn and Hazel and their family namely, Noel, Allan, Sylvia and Vivien were to subsequently reside at

Esmor House, The Beeches and Glasfryn Rhosesmor.

By 1939 the Jones brothers ran the largest threshing baling business in the County of Flintshire. They ran at least ten threshing

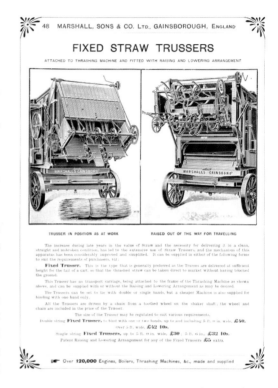

RIGHT: T.A Wynne Edwards of Denbigh N. Wales manual Hay and Straw Press 1885.

1893 Chester Royal Show
Wynne-Edwards of Denbigh Hay Press

sets with work extending as far as the Wirral and into Cheshire. George Stephen Williams worked for Halkyn United Lead Mines as a blacksmith. With the running down of the mine he started to work for Jones Brothers on a part time basis. It is well known that he was the "brains" behind the design and development of all Jones pick-up balers. He rose to become Head of Design and Development or "The Experimental" as it became known.

The Second World War broke out with the government needing to increase food production. A million extra acres was put to the plough and so threshing and baling work increased. To meet this demand the Jones Brothers ordered a baler from Powells. War work meant that materials and labour was diverted to making armaments and that there was no hope of a baler.

Building Balers
In January 1942 Glyn and David set about building their own machine. It was designed

ON LARGE WHEELS FOR EASY TRANSPORT

The Davies hay and straw baler made at the Atlas Works in Shrewsbury baler was advertised in a 1941 farm machinery magazine.
Top:

FIG. 2.—Edwards's Hay and Straw Box Baling Press.

in the living room and built outdoors. Seeing that their ideas worked they set up a workshop a few hundred yards away at the old Rhosesmor Lead Works. Steel could only be purchased in small quantities of 15 cwt with a permit and other parts bought as spares from Howard of Bedford. Drilling machines, an electric welder and gas cutting gear was sought. By the beginning of June the first Jones Baler was completed. The cost of building it had put a strain on their finances, it was sold together with one of their old balers. John Williams Glaslyn Foundry in Porthmadog and Jones and Jones of Flint started casting gears for the next machines. Three more balers, making a total of four were built and sold to buy more equipment. In 1943 they made 12

machines mainly built by Tom (Ginger) Harry Williams and George Blackwell during the summer months whilst continuing to thresh in winter. Eluned Jones (now aged 91), the youngest sister of Glyn and David recalls going up from their little farm to paint these early balers.

By 1944 it was clear that their own contracting business was in competition with customers using Jones balers. The new model of baler was named "Tiger". Thus Jones sold their threshing machines to Arthur Hughes of Aston Hill, for the first time they had money to invest in staff and tools.

Ruddington south of Nottingham became a

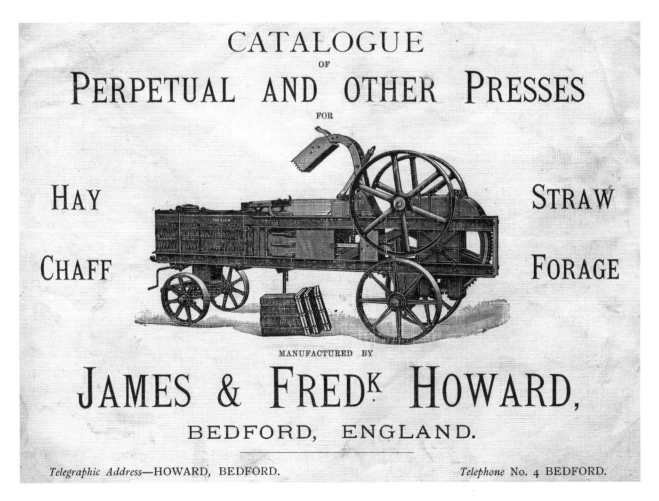

Mecca for Glynne and David. It was from here that the government released surplus war equipment from machine tools to Jeeps. Much of the Esmor Works was set up using war machinery a case of "swords into balers".

The road ahead however was far from easy. To quote Glynne Jones "We could now afford to employ engineers with better qualifications than what we had, but labour was very difficult to obtain. Though the war had finished in 1945 the de-mob period took a long time. We were looking for ex-RAF and army personnel with training in engineering that we could convert to our requirements. We had made do with men like ourselves who were willing to have a go, to learn along with us to produce what we thought was the right thing. Many were horse-men, cattle-men, sheep-men, men off the farms. They were very good and adapted to any job. Materials remained scarce, especially finished products such as tyres and bearings, we would start building a machine and complete it a month later". On the subject of labour a tribute must be given to the ex-German Prisoners of War who married local Welsh girls and rose through the ranks at Jones. Karl Hofmann

LEFT: Rhosesmor village and spoil heaps of Esmor lead works (Jones Balers) to the right.

BELOW LEFT: Esmor Works (Jones Balers).

BELOW LEFT: Esmor Works Staff 1942 note the lead mining waste. Left to right Tommy (Ginger) Jones, not known, David Jones, boy with cap Tom Williams (brother of George), Glynne Jones, George Williams. Baler in background.

BOTTOM: One of the first machines a mix of wheels weighing over 4 tons with no brakes! Note the early logo of a star.

TOP: Glynne and David admiring their work. Note the sign writing the work of Jack Jones who had only one arm. Machine fitted with brakes.

ABOVE: Miss Ena Young Wages Clerk.

ABOVE RIGHT: Early Tiger baler rubber tyres still no brakes.

was a POW at Pool Park near Ruthin and became General Manager at Mold.

The Jones Brothers also had the foresight to see the value of apprenticeship. The Esmor Works now comprised of several departments such as drawing office, tool room, research and development. A small foundry run by Wally Thompson was to follow but this closed in the early 1950s and all castings bought in.

Women were employed in all aspects of the works, from wages clerks to assembly and all the painting of the machines done by a team of ladies. Several disabled having lost limbs in the war were engaged in minding semi-automatic lathes and other suitable work. Life was hard in the villages that circled Halkyn Mountain. The lead mines had closed and people were only too glad of work at balers earning 9d an hour for a 48 hour week. Saturday morning 7.30 am - 12 noon. Philips Coaches from Hollywell ran a service that arrived for all to start at 7.30 am. A person more than 3 minutes late was docked 15 minutes pay. By 1950 Jones employed about 160 persons turning out 10 machines per week. Almost all the balers were sold on the home market.

Tiger
MODEL

HIGH-DENSITY SELF-FEEDING HEAVY DUTY
WIRE OR TWINE-TYING STATIONARY BALER

TOP: Tiger brochure with the Welsh Dragon Logo.

BOTTOM: Letterhead.

'Phone : HALKYN 248

ESMOR HOUSE,
RHOSESMOR,
MOLD, N.W. 12 th. April. 1943.

M. The Manager, Messrs. The Denbigh Mental Hospital, Home Farm, Denbigh.

JONES BROS.

Agricultural Engineers.   Threshing Machine Proprietors.

Hay and Straw Baling Contractors.   Haulage Contractors and Makers of Hay and Straw Balers.
Acetylene and Electric Welding, etc.

GJ/DL.

Dear Sir;

We should like to inform you that we have a
Tractor Machine & Baler working in your district, and would
be very pleased to do your work for you; the Terms are as follows:—
Tractor Machine & Baler both fitted with Self Feeders & Chaff Bagger
on Machine ;
Two Men supplied by us, also Wires, Oil & Fuel at £.8-10-0 per day,
less 5% for cash.

Chapter 2

STATIONERY HAND TYING BALERS

The Tiger
Stationary Baler Self-Feed Hand Tying Wire or String

With an overall length of 18 feet and weighing over 3 tons this was a "Goliath". In reality it was no heavier than the competition some weighing in at over 4 tons.

The threshing contractor had potentially a weight problem. Trussers were light machines and made what we called "battens" tied by two strings and was easily towed behind the thresher by one tractor. The combined weight of thresher and baler would now be over 6 tons and in hilly country could prove dangerous. The answer lay in pulling each machine separately using two tractors. In the stack yard the combined set was far longer, giving problems when "setting-up" especially on the smaller farms.

Small farms were also chopping straw for bedding and feeding the cattle, the straw chopping machines of the day were not designed to cope with bales. Farms had lofts in which sheaves or "battens" had been stored, pushing in high density bales through a doorway 8 feet up was no fun. The extra weight also posed some danger; farms were now becoming more mechanized and storage of machinery a new problem. Bales took less room in the barn and by leaving the outside walls intact could be used as shelter. The bales made by the "Tiger" measured 17 x 22 inches could be made to any desired length and weighed about 85 lbs, they could be tied by wire or string. On a pick-up baler the tying takes place when the bale is being compressed by the ram. Hand-tying balers basically rely on a long bale chamber to aid compression. Note the strings are slack at first and tighten as the bale expands and comes out of the baler. A long bale chamber means a big heavy baler. Its slow ram speed of 28 strokes per minute meant hefty engineering to cope with the volume of straw that came out of a thresher.

During war time due to shortage of rubber, early machines were fitted with steel wheels and no brake drums. Later, hand brakes were fitted as standard. An elevator could be supplied at extra cost, price £534-10s-0d (last listed available on price list dated December 1956). Sales of the Tiger would probably have peaked at around 1948-9 with contractors opting for the smaller Cub or the self-tying Panther. In the ten years 1944-1954 around 600 Tigers were built. It is estimated that less than 20 have survived into preservation in the UK.

August 1952   **TIGER**
Stationary baler with dual purpose needles
  for wire or twine.
Price : £534. 10s. 0d.

"TIGER MODEL" with ELEVATOR (Separate Unit)

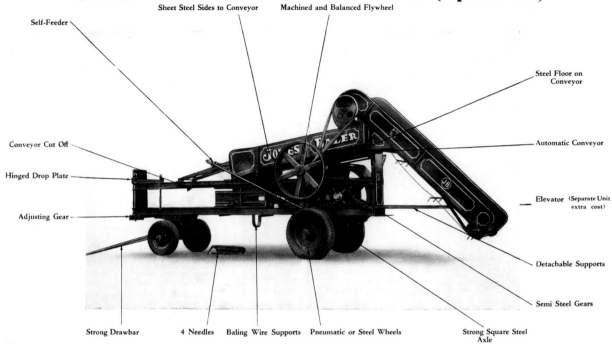

Self-Feeder

Sheet Steel Sides to Conveyor   Machined and Balanced Flywheel

Steel Floor on Conveyor

Conveyor Cut Off

Hinged Drop Plate

Adjusting Gear

Automatic Conveyor

Elevator (Separate Unit extra cost)

Detachable Supports

Semi Steel Gears

Strong Drawbar   4 Needles   Baling Wire Supports   Pneumatic or Steel Wheels   Strong Square Steel Axle

JONES' HAY AND STRAW BALERS

The above Illustration is reproduced from an actual photograph of one of our Balers, mounted on Pneumatic Tyres. Machines are also supplied on Steel Wheels or as stationary machines.
Specification Overleaf.
All Illustrations, Measurements, etc., are not binding, and are subject to alteration at any time.

WILLIAM ELDER & SONS. LIMITED
BERWICK-ON-TWEED

WILLIAM ELDER & SONS. LIMITED,
BERWICK-ON-TWEED.

LEFT: Land army (landgirl) wire tying.

The Cub
High Density Self-Feeding Wire or Twine Tying Stationery Baler

Introduced in 1945. Priced at £494 10s The   "Cub" was a lighter more compact version

RIGHT: 1950 Cub
advert.

BELOW: Cub a
smaller version of
the Tiger, the Dragon
appears.

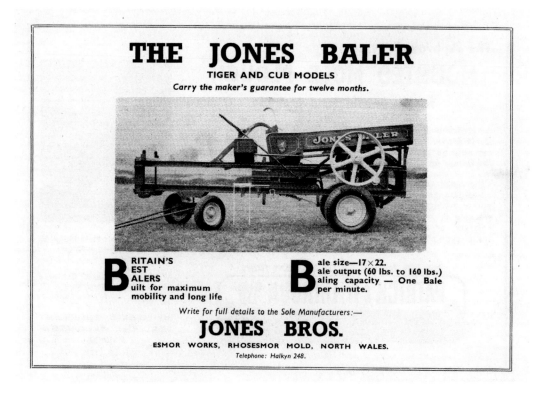

THE JONES BALER
TIGER AND CUB MODELS
Carry the maker's guarantee for twelve months.

BRITAIN'S **B**EST **B**ALERS uilt for maximum mobility and long life

Bale size—17×22. **B**ale output (60 lbs. to 160 lbs.) aling capacity — One Bale per minute.

Write for full details to the Sole Manufacturers:—

JONES BROS.
ESMOR WORKS, RHOSESMOR MOLD, NORTH WALES.
Telephone: Halkyn 248.

August 1952   **CUB**
Stationary baler with dual purpose needles
for wire or twine.
Price : £494. 10s. 0d.
(The Tiger and the Cub can be supplied
with one-man twine-tying needles).

of the "Tiger".

Tiger.

The chamber dimensions at 16in x 22in means that it makes a slightly smaller bale. Weight at 2 tons, 1 ton 5 cwt lighter than

Overall length at16ft, 2ft shorter than Tiger. Overall height at 5ft 3in it was a foot lower than Tiger. During the 1940s and

50s sweeping hay to a baler became popular, the lower height of the "Cub" was appreciated when forking all day from ground level.

The feed to a stationary baler has to be temporarily stopped whilst "needling" on commencing the baler has to cope with the additional straw from the thresher. Could the "Cub" with it's lighter flywheel cope?

The "Cub" proved to be an immediate success, it performed equal if not better than the larger heavier balers.

The addition of the "Collinson System" (See Collinson) further improved performance

RIGHT AND BELOW: Scenes from the Esmor Works, in Summer machines were finished outdoors.

and from becoming an option was almost the standard on most "Cub"balers.

The "Cub" was listed in the December 1956 price list still at £494 10s.

By the mid fifties threshing was in decline and the sales of hand tying static balers dwindled to a trickle.

Many were cut up their wheels and chasis converted into trailers.

Between 1945-55 up to 900 Cub balers were made.

Machines in preservation

At the time of writing about 10 machines are known to exist I am sure that there are a few more.

LEFT AND BELOW: Cub plate.

BELOW: Show Time. Left to right. Glyn Morris, Emlyn Lloyd, J.M. Jones, George Williams, Herbie Ellis, Bob Edwards.

Collinson's Twine-Tying Conversion Unit
(Patent No 637410)

Today, Collinson's Feed Hoppers are almost a feature of every farm. Jonathan Collinson and Sons of Lingart Farm, Barnacre, Garstang, Lancashire amongst other things were threshing contractors. Their literature states: "A System with Many Advantages"

Only one operator is needed, his work is reduced to a minimum, and he does not have to go to the other side of the baler at all, or even to the end of the baler to retrieve needles. As the engagement of the string is automatic and positive, baling can proceed at the usual speed.

* Agricultural Wages 1946 - £4 per 47 hour week.

RIGHT: Collinson.

For Quick and Easy Baling

COLLINSON'S TWINE-TYING CONVERSION UNIT

Is the BEST !

TWINE IS HARMLESS TO ANIMALS AND IS EASIER TO USE THAN WIRE IF YOU USE OUR PATENTED SYSTEM, BECAUSE—

1. Only ONE Light Needle is used.
2. No back wiring or needles to retrieve.
3. Fully automatic and positive threading of twine.
4. Bale size according to requirements.
5. Can be easily fitted to any Baler. No holes to drill.
6. Foolproof.
7. No fragile parts.
8. Low initial cost.

THIS SYSTEM IS BEING USED VERY SUCCESS-FULLY AND IS 100% IMPROVEMENT ON ALL OTHER METHODS.

J. COLLINSON & SONS
GARSTANG, PRESTON,
LANCS.

The Jones Brothers "Victory Loader"

The Jones brothers had not forgotten their days as farm labourers, forking tons of manure on to a cart and then spreading it. Loaders were in use at the nearby Rhosesmor Sand and Gravel Works, these would probably be Chaseside mounted on the Standard Fordson tractor.

The Esmor Works had heaps of lead waste surrounding it. In order to increase production of balers these had to be moved. What was needed was a loader, in true fashion the Jones Brothers set about designing and building their own. Thus emerged the "Victory Farmyard Manure Loader".

The "Victory" unlike industrial loaders could, it is claimed, be easily put on and taken off the tractor using only six fixing bolts. Although specifically designed for loading farmyard manure by attaching a scoop, it could load sand and gravel, hay and straw bales. The loading capability was approximately twelve farm cart loads per hour.

A belt from the tractor pulley drove a reduction gearbox, from the gearbox a drove a rope drum via a clutch and brake. The manure fork is hauled up the jib by a wire rope wound around the drum. The operator stood on the tractor, one lever operated the clutch/brake system and another, the fork/scoop trip. It could lift up to 10 cwt in weight to a height of 6ft 8in. The loader was granted various patents, the first applied for on April 20th 1944. It is worth noting that the patent is in the names of Glyn and David Jones. On approval, the Patent Office have returned many documents using Glynn and

Glynne Jones. It appears that Glyn adopted the Glynne version so I shall from now on refer to Glyn as Glynne Jones.

The Standard Fordson was heavy on the steering without a loader, it would have taken a monumental effort with a loaded fork of manure. The loader was initially only available for the Fordson tractor.

In 1945 Fordson brought out a new tractor the E27N. The following year hydraulic lift was available. Tractor hydraulics meant hydraulic loaders and a host of manufacturers started manufacturing. Names like JC Bamford MIL, Skyhi and Horndraulic to name but a few.

Thus the "Victory" was consigned to retirement.

TOP: Victory Loader at Rhosesmor.

JONES' VICTORY FARMYARD MANURE LOADER

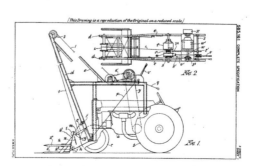

LEFT: Victory Loader as fitted to Fordson tractor.

RIGHT: Loader drawings.

Hammer and Roller Mills

During the Second World War David Jones (DT) had a smallholding on which he raised pigs. These were probably fed on the seconds grain obtained when threshing, this of course needed milling so a mill was built. Building small mills became a sideline to baler production. At this time sides of bacon and ham would have been useful as a bargaining tool when steel and machine parts were difficult to obtain!! How many mills were made is unclear as they are not on any price list. It is thought that this venture probably only lasted a few years between 1945-1949.

RIGHT: Roller Mill made by Jones.

BELOW: Headed paper.

INVOICE No. 1498

8532

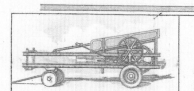 **JONES BROS.**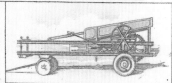

PARTNERS: D. T. JONES & G. JONES

AGRICULTURAL ENGINEERS &
MANUFACTURERS OF THE J.Bs HAY & STRAW
BALING PRESS & J.Bs HAMMERMILLS

**ESMOR HOUSE, RHOSESMOR, MOLD,
N.WALES.**

TELEPHONE Nº HALKYN 248.
TELEGRAPHIC ADDRESS: "JOBALERS, MOLD"

30th December 19 47

Mr. Pritchard,
Engineers Dept., Mental Hospital, Denbigh

Date	Your Order No. Verbal	Ours Z.720	Despatched per Pass.Train.22.12.47					
	Part No.	DESCRIPTION OF GOODS						

Chapter 3

PICK-UP BALERS

"I can't afford to look for trouble — that's why I'm looking for a JONES BALER..."

THE **JONES** MINOR MARK II

— and how's this for an end product?

Due to the clever patented design of the bale chamber, the Minor Bales are grooved at the top and base so that it is virtually impossible for the twine to slip off. This gives a positive saving in twine consumption and materially assists in aerating the stacked bales.

IT'S TOUGH, COMPACT AND MANOEUVRABLE

The minimum of moving parts, compact streamlined design and construction has made the MINOR MARK II a trouble-free robust " go-anywhere " money saving baler, easily handled under the most exacting conditions.

It is these " down to earth " commonsense factors which have made the MINOR MARK II such an attractive and profitable proposition for both farmer and agent alike.

If you are an agent and do not already represent us, why not contact us NOW?

MANUFACTURED BY

JONES BALERS LTD

MOLD, NORTH WALES Tel. HALKYN 363

A BIT OF HISTORY

Up to the 1930s hay would have been made by cutting, turning, tedding, windrowing made into cocks then carted into stacks or into a barn. The corn harvest was easier due to the widespread use of the binder which produced the tied sheaves. All of this was to change.

About 1936 a threshing contractor by the name of Ed Nolt from Lancaster, Pennsylvania sold his threshing outfit and bought one of the first Allis-Chalmers All-Crop combine harvesters. The farmers were not very pleased as they had no means of gathering the windrows of threshed straw. The straw was valued for feeding and bedding both cows and horses.

The Ummo Luebben pick-up baler made round bales and wrapped them in twine but was slow and unsuitable as a contractor's machine. The other choice was the Ann Arbor, it picked up the crop but needed two people riding on the baler to hand-tie. There was one more option; a man called Innes in Iowa had made a self tying pick up baler using knotters from a John Deere Binder using binder twine. Nolt bought one of these machines but found it very troublesome.

In 1937 Nolt built his own baler to be followed by another five the following year. Nolt was probably the first to build a baler that tied the bale whilst under compression, the system used later by all manufacturers. Nolt realized that "a proper baler twine" was needed. In 1940 the New Holland Company took over the Nolt Patents and started to mass produce the "automaton" the world's first successful pick-up baler. By 1945 Oliver had further developed the Ann Arbour and International Harvester were marketing the 50T. Claas had opted for the "low density" bales not popular in Britain for reasons discussed.

BELOW: David Jones checking the knotters.

LANZ

Straw and Hay Presses

Distributors:

LEFT: German built Lanz Press

The International 50T, a compact side feed machine priced at £711 was too wide and the auger tended to wrap with hay.

The Claas low-density baler priced at £585. A low output baler the bales being loose were not suitable for contract work. Jones had prided themselves as "Pioneers of British Built High Density Balers". In 1945-6 the Jones High Density "Pick–up Baler (Press) was trialled, it was the first self-tying pick-up baler to be designed and built in Britain.

Pick–up balers were being imported to Britain from America and Germany and the Ummo Luebben baler had been bought by Allis-Chalmers and was marketed as the "Roto-Baler". Driven from the tractor power take-off shaft and priced at £350! This was no contractor's machine as it required perfect windrows and was slow (had to put tractor out of gear to form a bale).

There is little doubt that Jones "borrowed" many ideas from Lanz of Germany. It is well known that their close friend George Denson of Henllan had a low density stationary Lanz baler and that frequent visits were made by the boys from Rhosesmor. A few German ex POWs, gifted engineers, were working at Rhosesmor - did they influence the design? We shall never know.

The New Holland "Automaton" priced at £895 worked well but was far too wide at over 10ft.

The Lanz design of swinging ram was beefed-up but unlike the Lanz, the ram working upwards into the baling chamber.

LEFT: The first all British built pick-up baler. "The Automatic Jones Pick- Up Press." Standing left to right. Rear, Glynne Jones, Corfield, J.M. Jones. Front George Williams, Roy Bennett, Fred Davis, not known.

The Jones Patent Tucker Knotter

Most American and German builders of balers had been making grain binders and had their own knotters protected by patents. Claas of Germany could have possibly supplied Jones but we must remember that in 1946 buying German would not have been the done thing.

Jones decided to develop and produce their own knotter called "The Jones Patent Tucker Knotter". This device has the Patent No 640,772, applied for on 19 August 1948. The "Tucker Knotter" was fitted to all Jones self-tying balers up to 1960.

Main Features

Jones argued that their knotter was more suited to making high density bales - bales that weighed between 65 and 85 lbs. Their theory was based on the fact that all other makers relied on the twine sliding between the formed bale and the new bale thus putting excessive strain on the twine and the retaining mechanism.

See diagram (other manufacturers)

Jones Tucker Knotter
How it works:

The tuckers were mounted on a shaft above the knotters. After a bale was tied the tuckers drew enough twine from the spools to form the top of the bale. The first charge of a new bale drew string from the spools but after the string at the end of the bale remained stationary. As the bale proceeds, twine for the bottom of the bale is fed from the spools. The tuckers move down paying out the twine for the top. When the tuckers are fully down (run out of string) they trip the knotters to tie the bale. By adjusting the starting point of the tuckers, the length of bale could be set. As far as it is known Jones were the only manufacturer to use this rather complicated system.

Summary:
- Tuckers feed twine to top of bale.
- Twine for bottom of bale fed through needles from twine spool.
- Twine between bales does not move.
- Twine length is relative to bale length.

WILL REVOLUTIONISE HIGH DENSITY AUTOMATIC BALING

Jones PatentTucker Knotter

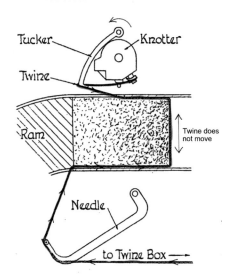

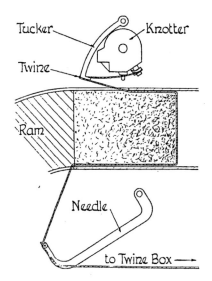

LEFT: The Jones knotter.

LEFT: Conventional.

Conventional Knotter (Rasspe)

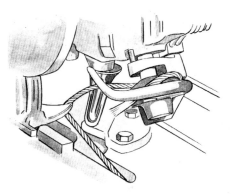

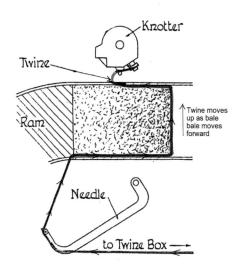

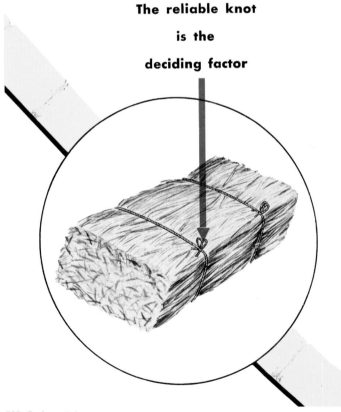

The reliable knot

is the

deciding factor

In the winter of 1947 the works at Rhosesmor was snowbound for weeks and fully engaged with the Tiger and Cub. It was decided to contract out building half of the thirty pick-up presses planned for the 1948 harvest. The work was given to AB Blanch and Co of Malmesbury Wiltshire. If all went well, then for 1949 Blanch would make 250 units destined for the south and Rhosesmor 250 for the north. The price was set at £850.

The balers produced by Blanch were less satisfactory and had to be re–worked at Rhosesmor. This episode coupled with the harsh winter almost sent Jones into great financial difficulties. The early models had the engine mounted at the front where it was claimed to be free from dust. Coventry Climax petrol and Turner diesels were tried but at less than 20 hp were not powerful enough.

TOP: Early prototype
at work.

ABOVE: The low
density bale
produced by the
Lanz.

The Lion
Model AC/T Automatic Pick-up Baler

By the 1949 harvest the pick-up press was sorted out. It was called "The Lion". Priced at £1,000 the baler was shortened by about 4 feet and a David Brown VAK TVO engine of 35 hp fitted. It was designated Model AC/T (Automatic/ Twine). Very few tractors had power take-off to drive the baler so most pick-up balers had their own power units. This of course added weight and cost. "The Lion" scored over its rivals in several ways and soon became the contractors choice, even with a hefty price tag Jones could not turn them out fast enough.

Main Points and Patents

- Narrow width 8 feet, good for narrow lanes and field gates. This was to be a strong selling feature of every Jones baler.
- The "Famous Grooved Bale" a trade mark of all future Jones balers. Patent No 666,024 1 July 1949.
- The twine is recessed into the bales preventing twine slipping off when handling.
- A saving of approximately 20ft of twine per ton of crop baled.
- Grooves allow air to filtrate through the stack.
- The machine having evolved from the low–density (Lanz) had the gentle folding action on the crop noteworthy of this design.
- A Patent Twine Tension Cutting Device Patent No 703, 170 - 1951.
- This safeguards the needles and knotting assembly from any undue strain and subsequent damage which could result from knots or snarling of the twine.
- The patented retracting tine conveyor Patent No 685957. This system was adapted for use on all future Jones "Minor" series balers.
- Patent No 638612 dated 19 March 1949. Relating to retaining the material being baled during the non-compressing or return stroke of the ram.
- A work rate that no other baler could match.
- Built to last.

Disadvantages

- Price   Lion 1952 - £1,1147-2s-6d.
- Weight   Almost 3 tons
- Bales   High-density and very heavy.

LEFT: Lion.

FAR LEFT: John Starsmore of Wicken near Milton Keynes bought this Lion in 1950 and claims that it has made almost one million bales!

LEFT: Makers plate Lion No 189 belonging to John Starsmore.

The tractor wheels straddled the windrows and hay could drag under the tractor. Knotters were not entirely reliable, not visible from tractor seat so several mis-tied bales could be made with the driver oblivious to the situation. Often a young lad would ride on the baler either hand-tying the missed bales or shouting "stop" to the driver - so much for Health and Safety!

Jack Salisbury a contractor from Out Rawcliffe in the Fylde of Lancashire had an answer. When the bales were mis-tied a horn sounded, ingenious!
John Starsmore a threshing contractor of

Wicken near Buckingham like so many was a prolific user of Jones balers. He worked three Lion balers bought from the local Jones agent namely WJ Cooper of Newport Pagnell. Over the years John has owned almost every model of baler that Jones produced.

In 1952 when Jones brought out the Minor producing a lighter bale they were condemning the Lion to history and its sales declined.

In order to lift sales a David Brown Diesel priced at £1250 was offered.

RIGHT: "Thank You" Young Raymond (son of DT) at Post Office.

FAR RIGHT: Women Painters pose outside Esmor Works in front of a completed Lion. On the right is the show caravan
Left to right rear row. Greta , Eileeen Jones, Flo Smith, front row Ada Joyce, Dolly Hanson, Doll Roberts? Marie Evans (Foreman).

LION
Trailed, automatic twine-tying pick-up. Engine driven.
Price : £1,147. 2s. 6d.

CRUDWELL
BLANCH
FARM MACHINERY

A. B. BLANCH & CO. LTD., CRUDWELL, WILTS.

The last Lion's were probably made 1954-55 and last appeared for sale on the official price list 1 December 1956.
The contractor had turned his attention towards the Diesel engined Jones Minor priced at £798.

How many Lion's were built? Estimated is 1200-1500 machines.
When were they last used? Many up to 1958.

What has happened to all the Lion's? At almost 20 feet long it takes much storage so most were scrapped, axles and wheels used to make trailers.

How many have survived? At the time of writing six machines.

Conclusion

In 1963 Claas introduced the Maximum high-density baler and yes it had a swinging ram. Looking at a modern "Big Square Baler" swinging ram, tractor straddling row (in line) one can only remark that Jones in their basic design were way ahead of their time.

LEFT: Still snow. Photo circa April 1948 Rhosesmor Post Office.

LEFT: Named Lion.

The Panther
Model SA/T Automatic Self-Tying Baler

THIS PAGE: "How is it going George"? asks Glynne Jones. Panther baler under test at George Denson Pen Porchell Isaf Henllan Denbigh.

Described as a stationary, automatic twine–tying baler for engine or tractor drive. The Panther replaced the hand-tying machines

The Panther was basically a Lion usually minus the engine and the pick-up reel. Early photo show an engine powered Panther with the round twine boxes fitted below the chassis. It is thought that this was built in 1947-48 being one of the reworked Lions built by Blanch and that after hardly any engine powered models were built. It cost £698-15s-0d less engine. This price was to remain until production ended in about 1955. The Panther cost £200 more than a hand-tying Cub but of course saved the wages of a person at about £6 per week.

The machine weighed in at 2 tons 9 cwt.
How many were built? It is estimated that between 900 and 1100 were built.
When were they last used? Early 1960s
Number in Preservation? At the time of writing four.

PANTHER

Stationary, automatic twine-tying baler for engine or tractor drive.

Price : £698. 15s. less engine

ABOVE: Panther
Price List.

TOP: Panther under
test.

RIGHT: The Show.

BOTTOM: At the
Show circa 1949.

LEFT: Panther under test.

CENTRE LEFT: Prototype "Panther" baler. Note engine driven, steel channel frame, U type front axle.

BOTTOM LEFT: Advert Panther.

BOTTOM: Production Panther with rolled steel chassis frame, modified front axle. Early models had round twine boxes twine.

OUT-PUT UP *labour costs down ....*

★ ENDLESS CHAIN CONVEYOR - CONSTANT FEED

★ AVOIDING INTERRUPTIONS AND WASTAGE

★ OF TIME USUALLY NECESSARY FOR NEEDLING

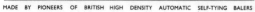

SIDE VIEW SHOWING POWER UNIT
WHICH IS FITTED IF REQUIRED

MADE BY PIONEERS OF BRITISH HIGH DENSITY AUTOMATIC SELF-TYING BALERS

THIS PAGE: Jones
Service Van.

JON

JONES BALERS

SERVICE   VAN.

Esmor Work

The Invicta
Model SP/T Self-Propelled Automatic Self Twine Tying High Density Pick-up Hay and Straw Baler

The World's First Self-Propelled Pick-up Baler 1949-1956
From the Latin *Invictus* – undefeatable : victorious

The Invicta in essence was a self-propelled Lion, therefore the baling part of it was already tried and tested, most of the new development centred around the transmission to the driving wheels and driver controls.

RIGHT: The "Invicta".

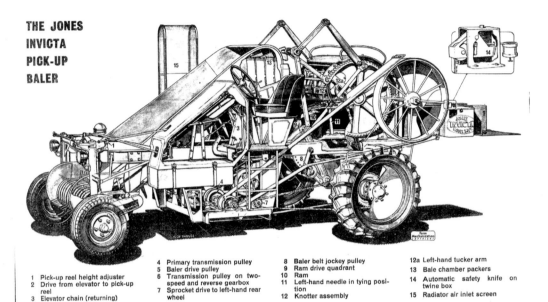

THE JONES INVICTA PICK-UP BALER

1 Pick-up reel height adjuster
2 Drive from elevator to pick-up reel
3 Elevator chain (returning)
4 Primary transmission pulley
5 Baler drive pulley
6 Transmission pulley on two-speed and reverse gearbox
7 Sprocket drive to left-hand rear wheel
8 Baler belt jockey pulley
9 Ram drive quadrant
10 Ram
11 Left-hand needle in tying position
12 Knotter assembly
12a Left-hand tucker arm
13 Bale chamber packers
14 Automatic safety knife on twine box
15 Radiator air inlet screen

RIGHT: John Rennie Jones (Service Manager) on an early Invicta, note lead waste in background.

Self-propelled meant that it came under the strict road regulations, under 8ft wide, licensed, and had to have a number plate, lights and horn.

The prototype was 8ft 3in over the hubs and so began a battle of words. Jones protested that the other balers of American origin over 9ft wide were frequently towed on British roads. The situation was resolved and work progressed during the winter of 1949.

The machine made its first appearance at the Chester County Show held in June 1950 and gained a Silver Medal.

The Royal Agricultural Society of England (RASE) was established in 1838 with its motto "Practice with Science". It conducted "the Annual Trials of Machines" and some of these reports make fascinating reading. It is interesting to note that in 1887 at the Newcastle upon Tyne trials a North Wales company namely Powell Brothers and

FAR LEFT: The "Invicta".

LEFT: High speed bailing.

BELOW: Headlights were compulsory, taxed for the road.

RIGHT: Tommy (Ginger) Jones driving the production model – raised cooling air intake, twine boxes on side of bale chamber.

BELOW: The Competition at the R.A.S.E. Trials.

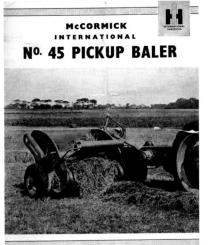

TOP LEFT: "Look at what my dad built" a smiling David Jones (DT) with son Raymond Ellis Jones now of Flintshire Caravans.

TOP RIGHT: The Royal Welsh Show at Abergele 1950.

ABOVE LEFT: Headlights were compulsory, taxed for the road.

LEFT: The Competition at the R.A.S.E. Trials.

OPPOSITE BOTTOM: The Jones Team. Left to Right. Herbert Ellis– Head Storeman, E.G. (Bert) Powell – Draughtsman, Robert (Bob) Edwards – Chief Draughtsman, Roy S. Bennett – Design and Sales, John Merfyn Jones – Purchasing Manager, Glynne Jones – Managing Director, Emlyn Lloyd Company Secretary, Walter Frederick (Fred) Davis –Works Manager, William(Bill)Davies Production Foreman, George Stephen Williams – Chief Design Engineer.

Whitaker of Wrexham gained the RASE first prize and a cheque of £20 for their potato digger - but that is another story!

The RASE announced that their forthcoming trials of 1950 was to be at Shillingford, Oxford. The title "Forage Harvesting Machinery Competition", total prize money for all classes £3,000!

There was renewed interest in silage and artificial green crop drying as a means of grass conservation. The minimum wage had risen to £5 per week and there was greater stress on machines to do the heavy work. There was also a feeling of over reliance on

importing machinery from America.

Class A of the competition was reserved for machines in or ready for manufacture, for the collection and disposal of hay and straw from a windrow.

Jones entered the Lion and Invicta High Density. Other entrants were No 45 International Harvester, Mc Connel Jay, Salopian 45, and Lorant (Low Density).
The trials took place over several weeks with the machines having to deal with a variety of windrow and crop conditions.

The two machines which impressed the

RIGHT: At the trials. The poor weather conditions favoured the Invicta. Glynne Jones with camera, Cyril Mason watching the knotters, George Williams at the wheel, David Jones (DT) to the right.

RIGHT: "Top Team" L-R John Rennie Jones, Cyril Mason(Tool Room Manager), Glynne Jones, David (DT) Jones, Bob Edwards, John Merfyn (JM) Jones.

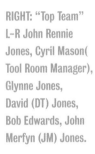

RIGHT: Glynne Jones Managing Director receiving R.A.S.E. Gold Medal, his brother D.T. looks on.

FAR RIGHT: Herbie Ellis congratulates Glynne Jones. £750! About £30,000 in to-days money. No wonder they are smiling.

LEFT: Invicta.

BELOW LEFT: The Certificate.

BELOW: R.A.S.E letter.

Royal Agricultural Society of England

FORAGE HARVESTING MACHINERY COMPETITION 1950

Class A

Machines, in or ready for manufacture, for the collection and disposal of hay and straw from the windrow

FIRST PRIZE

awarded to

JONES BROS.

Rhosesmor, Mold, N. Wales.

for

"Invicta" self-propelled baler

ROYAL AGRICULTURAL SOCIETY OF ENGLAND
16 BEDFORD SQUARE, LONDON, W.C.1

SECRETARY: TELEGRAMS: TELEPHONE:
ALEC HOBSON, O.B.E.   PRACTICE, PHONE, LONDON   MUSEUM 5905 (5 lines)

P/E/P   6th October, 1950

Dear Sirs,

In forwarding the enclosed cheque for £750 as the amount of prize money won in our Forage Harvesting Machinery Competition, I would like to take the opportunity of conveying the Society's congratulations on such a manifest success.

Yours faithfully,

Secretary.

Messrs. Jones Bros.,
Rhosesmor,
Mold,
North Wales.

It is requested that all communications be addressed to the Secretary.

judges were the Invicta and the International 45. These machines were like chalk and cheese and there was difficulty in setting standards that meant fairness to both competitors.

David and Glynne Jones had in the Invicta a Goliath of a machine weighing over three and a half tons priced at £1,550. The Americans had a lightweight of just over a ton costing £575.

On the trial the Invicta travelled at over 4 mph and baled over 5 tons of hay per hour, the machine capable of baling up to six acres per hour. Bale weight averaged 75 lbs each. Not many know but during the event the axle bent and so an engineer by the name of William Evans (Will Corwen) spent most of the night machining a new axle of greater strength. Early next morning a lorry left Rhosesmor and the Invicta was back in action with no one being none the wiser. The Baler with the Dragon on its side breathed to fight another day!

The judges awarded the Gold Medal and cheque for £750 to Jones Brothers. The International 45 gained the silver Medal and prize of £300.

See Awards

BOTTOM: The Cheque.

In 1950 most of the baling in Britain was done by contractors where speed is all, to that end the result was fair. At the heart of the Jones was a Ford V8 petrol engine turning out 70 hp at 2250 rpm. Production machines had a Morris MEB Mark 1V developing 42 hp at 2250 rpm. This gave a field consumption of just over two gallons of TVO per hour.

The transmission

From a single plate the drive split in two, one to the baler via flat belt and jockey type clutch, the other to a pair of variable vee-belt pulleys drove through a 2-speed and reverse gearbox. The combination of pulleys and 2 speed gearbox gave a total of 24 forward speeds and 12 reverse. Any 12 changes could be made on the move. The change is made by a combined hand and foot pedal which increases or decreases the diameter of the driving (engine) pulley. The diameter of the driven (gearbox) pulley, varies automatically. If you are familiar

RIGHT: Invicta.

BELOW LEFT:
Celebration Dinner.

BELOW RIGHT:
Autographs.

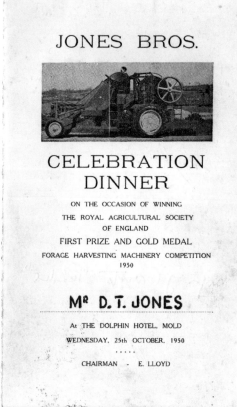

JONES BROS.

CELEBRATION DINNER

ON THE OCCASION OF WINNING
THE ROYAL AGRICULTURAL SOCIETY
OF ENGLAND
FIRST PRIZE AND GOLD MEDAL
FORAGE HARVESTING MACHINERY COMPETITION
1950

MR D. T. JONES

At THE DOLPHIN HOTEL, MOLD
WEDNESDAY, 25th OCTOBER, 1950
. . . . .
CHAIRMAN - E. LLOYD

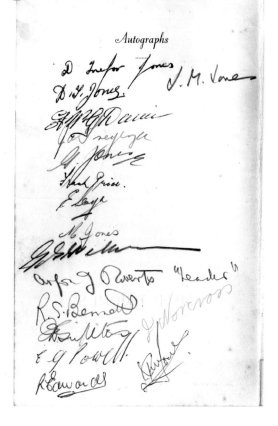

with combine harvesters of this era then no further explanation is needed. The first Invicta gearboxes were ordered as spares from Massey-Harris at Manchester. Jones soon found the foundry and original gear makers that supplied Massey!

The ability of the operator to drive the baler at its optimum forward speed was the ace in the Jones pack. In contrast the 45 baler was power-driven which at the time was ahead of the market but few tractors could operate

it to its potential as they lacked both power take-off and a range of forward speeds. The disadvantage of non-live power take-off is discussed in the next chapter.

During the trials the Invicta was driven by no less than George S Williams, Works Manager and Development Engineer.

Celebrations
Held at the Dolphin Hotel Mold, Wednesday 12 October 1950.

LEFT: Dinner Photo
Left:
Emlyn Lloyd – Co Secretary

Roy S Bennett – Sales

Arfon J Roberts – Flintshire Leader

Arnold Tregemza

J Rennie Jones

Right:
Bill Davies – Prod Foreman

J Glyn Morris – Buyer

J Jones

JM Jones

Fred Davis

A closer look at the Invicta

The Invicta was hailed as the Master of Harvesting and publicity material shows it performing several operations. It shows it towing a thresher and then powering it, thus saving the use of a tractor and giving the baler an all year use. It had a large turning circle and manoeuvrability in confined areas, condemned it to large fields. The 42 hp Morris MEB Mk4 engine in such dusty conditions overheated. Overheating reminds me of the Invcita that caught fire at a grass drying plant.

Drying of grass by artificial means probably reached its peak in the early 50s. Generous government grants and cheap fuel hastened their development. Ransomes, Templewood, and Alvan Blanch were amongst their manufacturers. Grassed aerodromes needed constant mowing and plants were set up. The grass was so short that it was not easy to bale and much was wafered (like shredded wheat). Well do I remember the sweet smell and clouds of steam from "The Grass Drier" at Bachymbyd on the A494 Ruthin Denbigh road!

Jones extolled the advantage of the Invicta in that it could operate slowly and gently thus folding the grass, leading to "no loss of leaf "or nutrient. However the combination of dried grass, a coke furnace and the Invicta's engine position proved to be a combustible mix and fire broke out. George Blackwell (Engineer) was heard to say. "At least it's the only baler that could

RIGHT: The Golden Baler at a Golden Price.

BELOW RIGHT: On it's way to The Queen at the Royal Farms.

BELOW: In 1951–2 Richard Lancaster built his own "Invicta look alike" from a Lion.

BOTTOM: The Lancaster baler used a Fordson engine and gearbox an was last used in 1959.

be reversed out to meet the fire engine"!

Mr Bill Lister of Attleborough, Norfolk is amongst the few Invicta owners. The machine No 103677 arrived in January 1952 and was last taxed for the road in 1963. During its life this also caught fire but was restored and repaired.

Invicta Success or Failure?

Just like Concorde the Invicta was fast, very fast and certainly got Jones noticed. Victorious it was, but winning a Gold Medal does not guarantee commercial success. The Silver medallist B45 now produced in England was the market leader. 1952 price list - Invicta £1608-10s-0d very expensive even for the contractor and its high density bales needed two people to lift them in the field or stack it's towed trailer.

*Note Agricultural Wage £5-13s-9d per 47 hour week.

A New Jones Minor baler and New Fordson Major tractor cost £400 less than the Invicta!!

Jones fitted a Perkins L4 but it was economy at further cost.

The Invicta appeared for the last time on 1 December 1956 price list.

It is estimated that less than 100 were built and very few after 1953. Of these about half a dozen have made it to preservation.

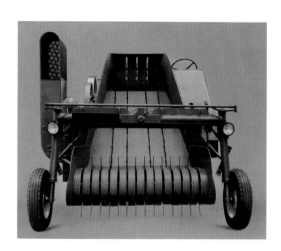

LEFT: Invicta under test at grass drying plant at Jones Balers Farm Sealand Manor.

Chapter 4

JONES MINOR – TOP OF THE CLASS

OPPOSITE: Show at
Newton Abbot Devon.

FARMER and STOCK-BREEDER, July 1-2, 1952

JONES BALERS
AT THE
ROYAL SHOW 1952
STAND 263
6th Avenue : Block F

GOLD MEDAL WINNERS 1950

SPECIALISTS IN THE MANUFACTURE OF BALING MACHINES

Winners of the R.A.S. of E. Gold Medal, 1950

INVICTA
The Gold Medal Winner 1950. The World's first Self-propelled Automatic Self Twine Tying Pick-up Baler. Built by the British pioneers of Automatic High Density Balers.

LION
The first British Automatic Self Twine Tying High Density Pick-up Baler.

Pioneers of British High Density Self Tying Balers

PANTHER
The first British Automatic Self Twine Tying Stationary Baler.

MINOR
A newcomer to our range. A Baler the Farmer can include amongst his implements with confidence.

There's a Jones Baler for every Farmer's need!

TIGER
The machine that has proved its value to both Farmer and Contractor.

CUB
Lightweight reproduction of the Tiger Baler. Its popularity cannot be fully emphasised here.

JONES BROTHERS
ESMOR WORKS, RHOSEMOR, Nr. MOLD, NORTH WALES.
Telegrams : JOBALERS MOLD.   Telephone : HALKYN 248.

CVS-15.

Background

At the Jones Brothers stand at the Cambridge Royal Show 1951 there was nothing new on offer. Meanwhile the American companies were forging ahead. International had the B45 in production in their UK factories. Massey Harris had the 701 at Kilmarnock. New Holland imported by Sale Tilney of Wokingham Berks were soon to become a strong player. John Wallace and Sons of Welwyn Garden City brought in the US made Oliver No 100. Jack Olding and Co Ltd the John Deere. Allis-Chalmers the Roto-Baler.

German makers Welger (Western Machinery) and Class in addition to their low-density machines were moving towards bringing in medium density balers. The British manufacturers seemed to be struggling. Ransomes at Watford with the RLP low density. Salopian at Prees with the Model E Mk2. Powell at St Helens with the "Monarch".

Unlike the German farmer British farmers did not take to the low-density baler or the bales. Even for the small farmer the baler

BELOW RIGHT: On test winter 1951–2 prototype Minor Mk1 driven via gearbox off thresher.

BELOW: Prototype Minor Mk1 note the long bale chamber.

was too slow - 2 tons per hour, the bales of strange dimensions and too soft. "Any rain and they are worse than loose hay" was the comment.

Both International and Massey Harris had proven that the medium density bale of standard size 14 x 18 x 30-36 long best suited British farmers. To be successful Jones would be wise to follow this route. Jones had pioneered high density baling but the farmer preferred the lighter bale that could be pitched by one man with a fork.

Jones were impressed by the B45 in1950-51 and set out to evaluate it (take it to bits and see how it worked). This task was given to George Williams and John Bumby at the now so called "experimental department" at Rhosesmor. John recalls a B45 fitted with the Jones tucker knotter to find out if it would accept a faster tying cycle. The new baler would have a ram stroke speed of 75 per minute as against the standard 45 of the Lion.

August 1952   **MINOR**

A new model introduced this year: trailed, engine or power take-off driven, automatic twine-tying pick-up baler, approx. 8 ft. wide.

Price : £658. 10s. 0d.

Each of the above machines produces a 36-in.-length bale.

BELOW RIGHT: Jones Balers Ltd.

DELIVERY NOTE

Telephone: HALKYN 248
Telegrams: "JOBALERS, MOLD"

JONES BALERS LTD.

Directors: D. T. JONES, G. JONES, H. E. JONES, Z. JONES

MANUFACTURERS AND ENGINEERS
BALER SPECIALISTS

B N? 7991

F. H. Burgess Ltd
Bridge Street.
Llangefni
Anglesey.

ESMOR WORKS, RHOSESMOR, MOLD
N. WALES

23/6 1954

YOUR ORDER No. 5945 OUR 7316 DESPATCHED PER Post.

The Jones Minor Mk 1

Three new Jones balers were built for the winter of 1951 and named Jones Minor Mk1 or Model SF/T. Some had gearboxes driven by belt from the threshing machine fitted and spent all winter on test baling straw. Jones had noted the weaknesses of the competition and set out to build the best in its class. The American Balers in particular were too wide for narrow gateways and the sunken country lanes where Jones tested, the most compact the B45 was 8ft 9in wide, even the Prees built Salopian was 9ft. Jones up to 1960 designed balers that could go through an 8ft gateway with stone gateposts.

American balers "do not like British hay," it causes wrapping and blocking of the conveyor and cross feed auger. Jones adapted from the "Lion" the cross feed with patented self-cleaning tines. This would be for the next years a feature of all Jones balers. Jones wisely offered its new baler with a range of options, power take-off driven, engine driven, or belt driven from thresher. Its basic weight was 1 ton 6 cwt and aimed at the farmer as well as contractor priced at £658-10s-0d (pto model) and £798-10s-0d (with Diesel Engine).

This price compared very favourably with the competition B45 £638. The B45 being a power driven machine was ahead of its time but as seen in the previous chapter "to be different is risky". The vast majority of tractors in use on our farms had no power drive and only a three speed gearbox! Thousands of Standard Fordsons and many E27N Majors fell into this category. Most Nuffield and David Browns had power take-off, but the Brown was a little on the light side. The Ferguson was definitely light the T 20 had a non standard pto shaft and only 20 plus horses on tap. Contractors ran Olivers, International W9s, Field Marshalls, good towing tractors but hardly suited to power take-off work.

The New Fordson Major the EIADDN Diesel

introduced in 1951 with 40 bhp and a price of around £500 proved to be an immediate success with both farmer and contractor. Ford for some reason geared the pto to turn at the standard 540 rpm at only 1200 engine rpm. The engine was a good "slogger" but at these revs lacked power. Ford offered a solution, the external raised gearbox which meant the engine now ran at 1600 rpm. The main drawback of these tractors, the lack of "live" power take-off. When the clutch was depressed forward movement and both power-drive and hydraulics ceased to operate. The answer in the 50s was the "live" drive or dual clutch. Pressing the first stage stopped movement of tractor and baler, while still maintaining drive to the baler. Thus gear changes and temporary slowing down to adjust to windrow could be made.

I am sure that many of you have managed to bale acres without "live" pto-drive, by knocking the tractor out of gear when the baler rocked the tractor forward; waiting for the baler to run empty and re-engage gear. You became a master at rowing up with no lumps and freewheeling on gentle downward slopes - "happy days"!

The Minor made its first appearance at the 1952 Royal Counties Show at Guildford and then on Stand 263 at the Royal Show held at Newton Abbot. Jones now had a machine that could once again challenge the Americans. This new baler was also going to affect the sales of their own Lion and Invicta. More combine harvesters appeared, threshing declined and so did orders for the old Tiger and Cub stationary balers.

Up to now many Jones machines, had been sold and serviced direct from the Esmor Works Rhosesmor. Jones could sell all they produced. From placing an order to delivery it took months. Setting up a dealer network and exporting had not been given priority. To sell the Minor, Jones would need more dealerships both home and abroad. The B45 and MH 701 balers were tied to International and Massey-Harris and later Massey-Ferguson dealerships world-wide. Other manufacturers eyed the potential market through dealerships. One such company was Bamfords Ltd of Uttoxetter who in 1953 signed an agreement with the Long Corporation of America and imported the BL60. The BL60 was no match for the Jones but Bamford, a leading British machinery company had a good dealer base.

Jones, a family run business sought independent dealers that ran on similar lines to themselves.

1953 The formation of Jones Balers Ltd.
Directors: Mr Glynne Jones, Mrs Hazel E Jones (wife), Mr David Thomas Jones, Mrs Zillah Jones (wife).

ABOVE: Jones Balers Ltd.

LEFT: "On their way"
Mk2s on the new
artic trailers.

Minor Mk2 Automatic Pick-up Baler

The Mk2 was an improved version of the Minor Mk1, it incorporated several safety features found lacking on the Mk1.
It also incorporated the patented connecting rod Patent No 753037 filled with oil the reservoir automatically lubricated the crankpin and gudgeon–pin bearings.

RIGHT: Introduced by Petters in 1950 the Diesel AVA 2 air-cooled at 15 bhp. was the choice for the British market.

Official Price List 1 December 1956 Minor model Mk2

Fitted with Petter AVA 2 Diesel Engine 15 bhp.   £850-0s-0d
Fitted with Petter PAV 4 Petrol Engine 19 bhp.   £840-0s-0d
Fitted with Jap Petrol or Petrol/Paraffin Engine 12 bhp   £758-10s-0d
Fitted with Coventry Victor 12 bhp   £778-10s-0d
Fitted with Power Take-Off drive and clutch   £678-10s-0d

Between 1952-58 it is estimated that about 3000 Minor Mk1 and 2s were built.

In May 1957 J Mervyn Jones becomes General Manager of Jones Balers Ltd.

Jones Balers were now exporting to Australia, Canada, Denmark, France, Belgium, Holland, Germany, Luxembourg, Russia Switzerland, Italy.

In March 1958 JM Jones, their cousin, visited Australia and New Zealand. Australia had import restrictions, and to overcome these Jones were to consider manufacturing in Australia.

Engines fitted to Jones "Minor" Balers

Petter AVA 2 - 13 bhp Air Cooled Twin cylinder diesel engine.
Oetter Petter PH 2 - 15 bhp
Petter PAV 4 - 19 bhp Petrol
Jap 12 bhp petrol or petrol paraffin engine
Coventry Victor - 12bhp

Most imported or American pick-up balsers had petrol or TVO gas guzzling engines. By the early 1950s British farmers and contractors were buying diesel tractors and soon realised their economy and reliability. Jones wisely fitted Petter Diesel, the other options being available for export to say Austrralia where petrol was cheap.

The Self-Propelled SP Minor

Introduced in 1954. Priced at £1,125.

The machine is basically a "Minor" Mark 2 with a self- propulsion unit.

Described as:
- Highly manoeuvrable - a great time saver.
- 8ft overall width.
- Can be turned in its own length.
- Patent Tucker tying mechanism.
- Economical diesel power.

Details at a glance:

Power Unit	Enfield 20 bhp. Horizontally opposed twin diesel.
Transmission	Clutch and 4 speed reverse synchromesh gearbox.
Road Speed	1-10 mph.
Weight	2 tons 2 cwt approx.

Jones were determined to have another attempt at the idea of a self-propelled pick-up baler. The "Invicta" had enjoyed some success but the SP Minor turned out to be "almost a non-starter". Only five were built.

The Enfield Series 100 Diesel was a light engine of alloy construction and John Bumby recalls problems with cylinder heads working loose and low power. The machine would be to be a nightmare for Health and Safety today. Note upfront driving position close to the noise and fumes from the engine. It drove only one wheel.

Machines in Restoration:
This machine was new to AM Jones and Son, Bryn Nefydd, Henllan, Near Denbigh.
It had been converted to be pulled by a tractor, leaving the engine to power the baler.
Restored by John Jones and Glyn Jones the machine formed the centrepiece of Clwyd's display of vintage machinery at the "Royal Welsh Show" at Builth Wells July 2008.

John Bumby in the test and development at Rhosesmor, worked on this project.

THE JONES
S.P.Minor
MODEL

SELF PROPELLED AUTOMATIC
TWINE TYING PICK-UP BALER

JONES BALERS LTD.
ESMOR WORKS, MOLD, N. WALES.

Sole Manufacturers of the World's largest range of Balers.
Telephone **HALKYN 363**   Telegrams **JOBALERS MOLD**

ABOVE: S.P.Minor.

Football

In 1927 the "Llandyrnog and District Summer Football League was formed. Its aim was to give farm workers an opportunity of playing some form of organized games. As farm workers toiled 12 hours a day seven days a week Saturday sport was not possible. Given goodwill on part of their employers it was felt that the worker could possibly play football on one or two evenings during the summer months. Threshing was mainly a winter occupation and the young contractor namely Glynne Jones who showed great promise as a centre-forward however joined

Llanbedr in the Ruthin League. In 1938 they were league champions.

Glynne later played for Llangynhafal and is described as "an opportunist centre forward" and twelve years later aged almost forty played no small part in the team enjoying its best ever season. The team completed the season without defeat and also won the Champions versus "The Rest" match. Soon after Glynne hung up his boots and took up the sport of clay pigeon shooting with his partner and brother David.

Back: 2 D. JONES, 4. G. EVANS. 5. N. PLATT. 1. J.P. HUGHES. 3 E. ROBERTS. 6. T. EVANS.
Front 7 S. RUBEL. 8. J.C. JONES 9. G. JONES, 10. T. J HUGHES. 11. T. O'HARA.

ABOVE: July 1950 Llangynhafal Football Club, Ruthin and District Summer League Champions. Undefeated in the league and winning the annual Champions v The Rest by five goals to four.

Shooting

The North Wales Shooting School at Sealand Manor is world renowned and is run by Justin and Guy Jones the grandsons of Glynne Jones. In the past shooting and agricultural contracting seems to have gone hand in hand. Contractors used to carry guns on their tractors and woe betide a rabbit or pheasant! The sound of the machinery drove the birds to the centre of the field as it was harvested but sooner or later they would break cover and fall to the guns.

The world of clay pigeon shooting, the manufacture of cartridges and clays and the trap machines to throw them was dominated by the Imperial Chemical Company (ICI). With their increasing interest in the sport the Jones brothers were soon major buyers of cartridges. They approached ICI in an attempt at securing more favourable terms but were re-buffed. Not to be outdone in the early 1950s Glynne and David formed North Wales Traps and Targets based at Rhosesmor. In a corner of the baler works they set up a facility which made trap machinery and clay targets. The Jones brothers became Welsh internationals with Glynne narrowly missing on an opportunity

to represent Britain in the Olympics. In 1958 they held the first British Grand Prix of Olympic Trap, an event at which a young Jackie Stewart took part before being lured by motor racing. With him they established the Rolex/ Jackie Stewart Celebrity Challenge which raised hundreds of thousands for charities. This event continued in Scotland at the famous Gleneagles Hotel, where they established the biggest tuition only Shooting School in the world. Amongst the dozens of celebrities would be Prince Albert of Monaco, King Hussein of Jordan, British Royalty, and from the world of sport Bill Beaumont and Willie Carson.

It was at Sealand that Bob Braithwaite of Garstang honed his skills to win Britain's first gold medal of the 1968 Mexico Olympics. The British Grand Prix was held for a further thirty years with the world's best shooters appearing.

ABOVE: "Crack Shots" Glynne left and David right proudly pose in their Welsh International colours circa 1958.

BELOW: Early shoot at Rhosesmor circa 1953. Note on left Jones Balers service van and show caravan.

ABOVE: From The
Leader November
12th 1954. Welsh
clay pigeon shooting
team in Dusseldorf.
Standing third left
Glynne Jones, third
right Daid Jones,
right JM Jones.

RIGHT: "Aiming
High" Glynne Jones.

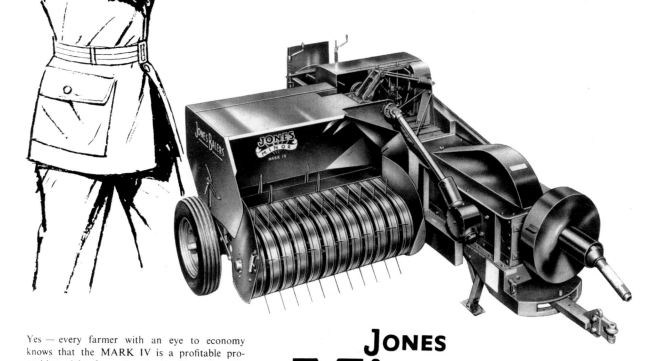

JONES BALERS
aim high too . . .

That is why you will find in the Jones Minor Mark IV—as in all other farm machinery from Jones Balers—a quality in design, material and construction which is second-to-none in the industry. And although Jones Balers aim high they still preserve 'down-to-earth' ideas such as a minimum of moving parts and compact streamlined design to give a trouble-free robust 'go-anywhere' baler, easily handled under the most exacting conditions.

Yes — every farmer with an eye to economy knows that the MARK IV is a profitable proposition right from the start! It's unbeatable in efficient performance, in low maintenance costs, and it's so compact! (Only 7′ 11″ overall width!) Ask your Agent to demonstrate the many worthwhile features incorporated in this fine machine.

JONES
Minor BALER
MARK IV.

THE JONES "CRUISER" COMBINE HARVESTER

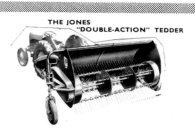

THE JONES "DOUBLE-ACTION" TEDDER

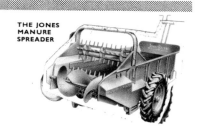

THE JONES MANURE SPREADER

ABOVE: Advert.

RIGHT: JM Jones who in May 1957 became General Manager of Jones Balers.

BELOW: Leaving for France.

John Merfyn Jones
known as JM (General Manager)

Career Profile
- Hydraulic Engineering Ltd
- Chester Engineering
- RAF Air Sea Rescue Service
- 1945   Jones Balers Rhosesmor (became Chief Buyer)
- 1957   General Manager of Jones Balers Ltd
- 1961   General Manager of Jones Balers/Allis-Chalmers Mold
- 1971?   Tiger Tim Firelighters in former Esmor Works, Rhosesmor

Hobbies
- Flying - had his own private aircraft
- Shooting

BELOW: Balers for Australia. Friday August 15th 1957 Mold Station. JM Jones General Manager sees off a consignment of Minor Mk2s.

JM was the son of Mr and Mrs John Jones of Plas Newydd Babell Near Holywell and first cousin of the Jones Brothers. As a boy I remember at the shows thinking that JM was Mr Jones Balers. Import restrictions imposed by Australia on fully built machines meant that Jones Balers were investigating the possibility of forming a company to manufacture "down under." In May 1958 JM went on an intensive export drive of six weeks to Australia and New Zealand. Discussions also took place with Baltic Simplex titled "the problem of trade restrictions". A large consignment of balers had been shipped to Australia the previous August.

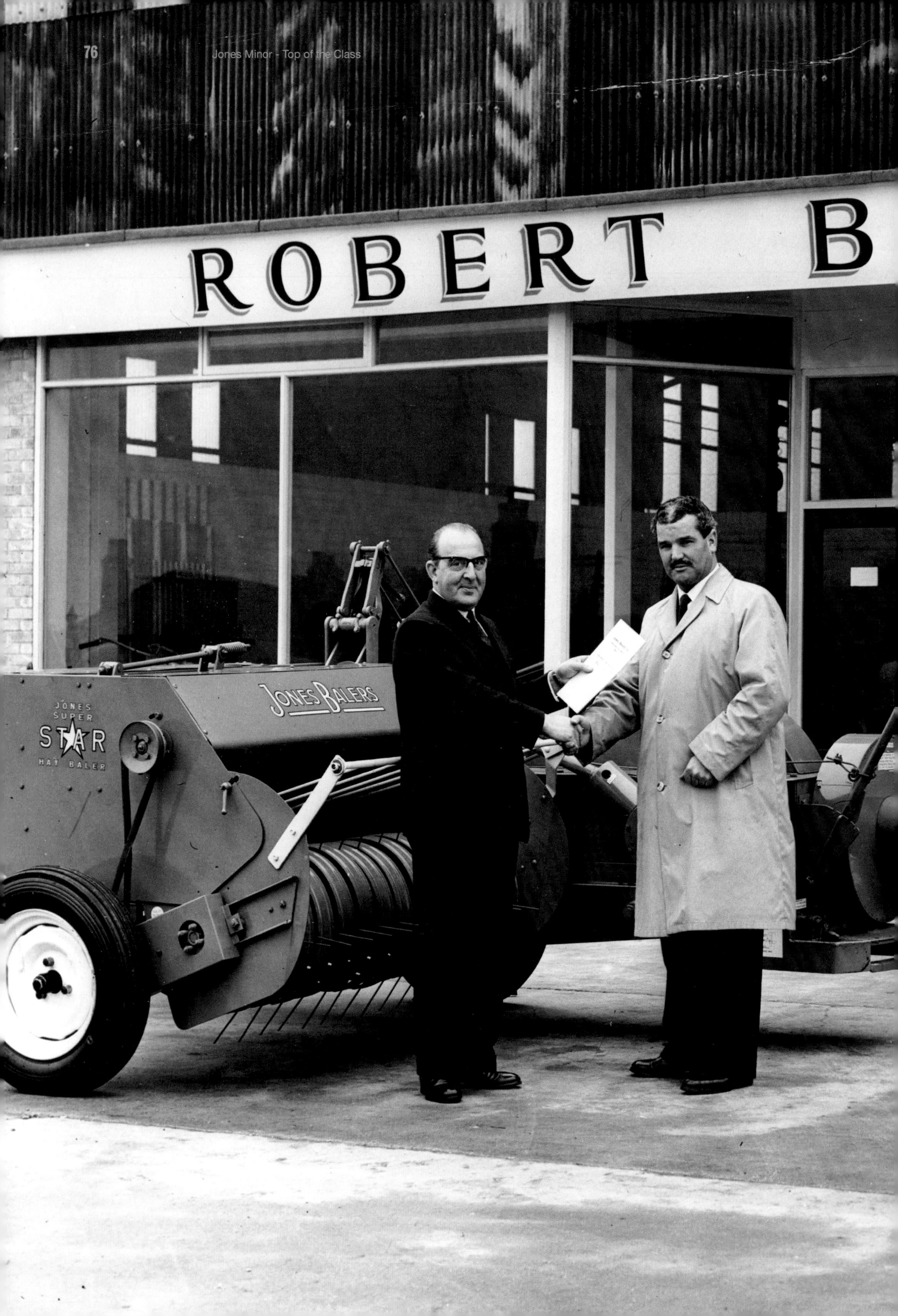
ROBERT B
JONES BALERS
JONES
SUPER
STAR
HAY BALER

LEFT: JM with Robert
B Massey who sold
hundreds of balers
in Yorkshire circa
1960 taking delivery
of a Super Star.

You save

The Jones Minor Mk.II P

You save TIME on maintenance for one thing, because
coupled with robust construction make the JONES a trou

You also save TIME because its compact streamlined d
anywhere" baler — easily handled under any conditions . .
FAMOUS GROOVED BALE tells its own story.

For the Contractor or large scale operator the JONES
features of its smaller brother plus OUTSTANDING OU

Why not get full details now?

Baltic Simplex Machinery Co. Ltd.

Please send me full details of the Jones
Baler.

NAME...

ADDRESS..

....

BALTIC SIMPLEX

Showrooms: 446-450

Offices and Factory: HAL

608-614 HARRIS ST., SYDNEY

ime and Twine

with a

Jones BALER

Available in PTO Model as illustrated or with Petrol or Diesel Engine. Each model has these outstanding, exclusive features:

PATENTED TYING MECHANISM

The Tucker Leg lifts a measured length of twine before the first charge enters the baling chamber. The leg is held in a poised position and as the first charge is pressed by the ram into the Baling chamber, more twine is withdrawn for the depth and base being formed, and gradually fed to the top of the bale. The bale base receives twine direct. As soon as the standard length is reached, the knotter mechanism is automatically tripped for tying. Result — no twine slip between bales, no twine strain and no knotter trouble.

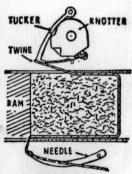

PATENTED BALE DESIGN

Due to the clever design of the bale chamber the bales are recessed top and base so that it is virtually impossible for the twine to slip off. This means a positive saving in twine. This illustration shows the patented design which forms the grooves at the top and base of the bale.

GROOVED BALE

Apart from making it impossible for the twine to slip off, these unique grooves also assist in aerating the stacked bales. Each charge is cleanly cut by a knife on the ram, thus giving a sliced bale.

On the farm SERVICE supports every Jones sale.

Model.

inimum of moving parts

e baler.

makes the JONES a "go-

d for TWINE saving the

is ideal — it has all the

ACHINERY CO. LTD.

ERS STREET, MELBOURNE

EET, SPOTSWOOD, VICTORIA

117 MERIVALE ST., STH. BRISBANE

Jones Baltic Propriety Ltd
Melbourne Australia

Western Mail Thursday 28 May 1959 "Mold firm to open up in Australia". An agreement signed at the Blossoms Hotel, Chester on 12 May saw the formation of Jones Baltic Propriety Limited, Melbourne. Following this agreement it seems that balers would leave Mold in "knock down" CKD form in for assembly at Baltic Depots in Melbourne, Sydney and Brisbane. The formation of the new company and this method of assembly probably qualified for the badge "Built in Australia?"

The waterproof crates were made by "No Nail-Boxes" of Saltney. The MP Gerald Nabarro (man with the big moustache and whiskers) was their Director.

Machines were crated at Mold and at Liverpool docks by the firm of AV Critchley.

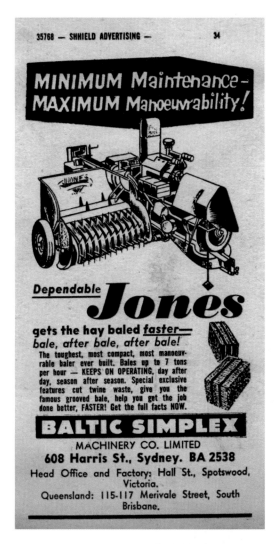

TOP LEFT: Wednesday 27th May 1959 Mold firm to open up in Australia. Jones–Baltic to manufacture Jones balers for the Australian market. Chairman and managing director of Jones Balers Glynne Jones signs agreement. Looking over left shoulder is TA Weston of Baltic Simplex. L to DT Jones director Jones Balers, Wayman Hales?, Bob Jackson auditor of Chester, RD Tyson, Emlyn Lloyd company secretary, JM Jones general manager.

TOP RIGHT: As top left with DT Jones signing Glynne Jones to left.

BOTTOM: Celebrating Success at the Dolphin Hotel Mold.

The Jones Minor MkIV 1958-1961

The Mk1V was just a face lifted Mk2 with a higher ram speed and the twine boxes at the rear of the pick-up reel. The New Minor Mk1V pick-up baler was introduced at the Smithfield Show in November 1958. It had been featured in the October issue of Farm Mechanization and Farmers Weekly.

BELOW: 1958 Testing the Mk1V.

Price of the standard pto-driven model £655 and fitted with a 15 hp Petter Diesel £840. By 1958 all the leading tractor manufacturers were offering "live power take-off" and the sales of engine powered balers became a trickle. The Mk 1V still had the "Tucker Knotter" which was now outdated. The whole knotter assembly comprised of over 200 parts. It was expensive to manufacture and sometimes needed constant "tinkering" to maintain it. Baling was still the province of the contractor and many by now had mastered the wizardly Welsh knotter. Other manufacturers were up-dating their

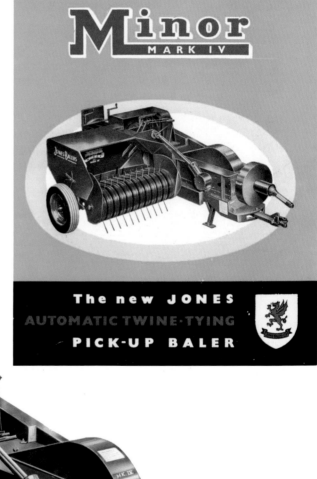

RIGHT AND BELOW:
The Jones Minor
Mk1V.

THE MINOR MARK II

IS EQUIPPED WITH THE *EXCLUSIVE* JONES PATENT TUCKER TYING MECHANISM

This unique system produces a bale as heavy as the standard twine can hold without the bales bursting. It is without comparison and its features will be recognised by the following sequence of operation. The Tucker Leg lifts a measured length of twine from the Twine Containers before the first charge of material enters the chamber. The leg is then held in a poised position by means of a specially designed control brake situated on the Tucker Shaft. As the first charge of material is pressed by the ram into the Baling Chamber it withdraws a further supply of twine from the twine containers for the depth and base being formed. The twine withdrawn is gradually fed to the top of the bale as the tucker returns with each succeeding charge. The base of the bale receives twine direct from the twine containers. When the bale being formed has reached the standard length of 36" the tucker automatically trips the knotter mechanism into operation for tying. The Jones Patent Tucker has proved its value by eliminating the need for the twine to slip between the bales. This applies particularly to the baling of new hay which invariably contains a high moisture content. The Tucker relieves the knotter twine retainer of all the strain to which it is usually subjected when holding the twine to be drawn between the two bales. In addition to this the twine itself is not subjected to any strain until the bale has passed out of the bale chamber.

Covered by the following British and Foreign Patents :—
GREAT BRITAIN : Pat. No. 640772. U.S.A : Pat. No. 2649043   AUSTRALIA : Pat. No. 143227. BRAZIL : Pat. No. 42142.
CANADA : Pat. No. 513043. ARGENTINE : Pat. No. 80709.   FRANCE : Pat. No. 1003901. GERMANY : Pat. No. 811413.
NEW ZEALAND : Pat. No. 102074.

BOTTOM: Merfyn
Jones (son of DT) on
the Fordson Dexta.
Note Live-Drive
badge on grille.

machines and were aiming their products at the farmer looking to buy his first baler. They fitted simple reliable knotters a route that Jones were soon to follow. The Jones had always been expensive and at almost a ton and a half in weight needed on the slopes, a tractor such as a Fordson Major was required. The New Holland Hayliner 68 built at Aylesbury proved to be a serious threat. It weighed just over one ton, and had a trouble free knotter. International Harvester had brought out the improved B-45 Mk2 and in October 1959 launched the B-46 priced at under £600. Within days British dealers had placed orders for over three thousand machines.

By 1961 International claimed that they had

sold over 40,000 British made IH balers to British and overseas farmers. Massey Ferguson introduced the lightweight 703 again aimed at the farmer. The Jones baler world was suddenly threatened by these huge American companies

During the summer of 1958 the Jones Mk1V final assembly line was set up at the new works at Mold. These early Mk1Vs were built by a small team from parts sourced from outside suppliers and Rhosesmor. Production of the Mk1V ceased in 1960. Jones stated that the Minor Mk1V was still available for the 1961 season. Between 1958-60 it is estimated that about 2500-3000 Minor Mk1Vs were built.

LEFT: "It will go through an 8ft gateway".

BOTTOM: A small tractor fitted with a Jones hitch can do the job.

The Jones Major Mk V and New Major Pick-up Baler 1956-1960

Introduced in 1956 the Major was a more robust version of the Minor Mk2. It featured a stronger gearbox, a longer throw on the crank, larger feed opening and three fingered packer. Bale dimensions of 14in x 18in was as Minor. "Designed for the large acreage Farmer and Agricultural Contractor". See Leaflet

BOTTOM: Prototype Major 1956 based on Minor Mk2 at Rhosesmor.

RIGHT: Jones Major brochure 1958.

Fitted with the splendid Armstrong Siddeley 20 hp diesel engine £898. By 1957 it cost £945 with a power take-off version at £785. Capable of producing a bale up to 100 lbs in weight. A self–propelled version of the Major was built (see photo). This high performance machine found its way to the farm of cousin John Ellis Jones at Nercwys near Mold.

In 1958 a New Major MkV version of the new Mk4 baler was introduced. Production ceased in 1960 with probably 500 built.

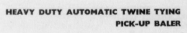

HEAVY DUTY AUTOMATIC TWINE TYING PICK-UP BALER

ARMSTRONG SIDDELEY

DIESEL ENGINE

FEATURES

AIR COOLING

SMALL DIMENSIONS

ACCESSIBILITY

LOW MAINTENANCE COST

RELIABILITY

LOW FUEL CONSUMPTION

14/22 HP

Manufactured by—
PETTERS LIMITED
CAUSEWAY WORKS,
STAINES, MIDDLESEX

A Member of the Hawker Siddeley Group

LEFT: Armstrong
Siddeley Diesel.

BOTTOM: Testing a
Major in the Vale of
Clwyd.

BELOW: Major
1958 fitted with
Armstrong Siddeley.
Cost almost £1000.

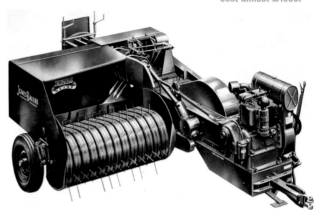

RIGHT: Major pto -
driven.

RIGHT: Major pto
model at Broncoed
Works Mold.

RIGHT: Threshing and
baling. Jones Pilot
combine and the only
Major self-propelled
baler built.

Chapter 5

EXPANSION –
NEW PRODUCTS
NEW FACTORY

The New Show Pavilion (20 June 1958)

Built for Jones Balers by AW Holmes of Mold.

Specifications
- Size - 60 x 40ft.
- Weight - 50 tons.
- Cost - £3,500
- Spec - main lounge, executive office, sales office, brochure office and refreshment facilities.

Use this year:
- Royal Highland Show Ayr.
- Royal Show at Bristol.
- Royal Welsh Show at Bangor.

Holmes transported and erected this pavilion for many years all over Britain.
The Paris and Smithfield shows supplied their own stands, and importers made their own arrangements elsewhere in the world.

Broncoed Park Works Mold

The Esmor Works was a series of long narrow home built corrugated sheds between mountains of lead waste. This meant that sub-assembly work could not be fed sideways on to the line. The demand for balers always outstripped production. A long waiting list can result in customers buying from another manufacturer, so in 1957 they acquired a 13 acre site on the site of the old Broncoed Colliery in Mold. The spacious Mold plant was purpose built as a baler production facility where sub–assembled parts could be fed on to a moving line. The works had a modern paint spray booth and a canteen. The main manufacturing and sales would be transferred to Mold with service, spares and development remaining at Rhosesmor.

BELOW LEFT: The new pavilion built by A.W.Holmes of Mold. Photo taken probably at the Royal Welsh at Bangor 1959. Left to right. Noel Jones (son of Glynne). Glyn Morris, sales. David Merfyn Jones.Glynne Jones, manging director. Elwyn Jones Fron Isa Farm, cousin of the Jones brothers.

LEFT: Last minute checks at the 1959 Royal Welsh Bangor. Foreground Major Baler engine driven priced at £945.

ABOVE. As left but in colour.

Daily Post 17 March 1959 - heading - "Balers make big move in one day". In truth balers had been coming off the line at Mold for months. The newspaper article has merely captured the final move of essential machinery from Rhosesmor. An extra 6d per hour was given to workers engaged in moving the machine shop as it involved weekend work. There were no large presses to move as Rhosesmor currently contracted out this work. The lathes and large pieces of machinery were lifted by their Coles RAF crane through a hole made in the roof. This was the trusty crane that had lifted thousands of Petter diesel engines onto Mk 2 and Mk1V balers. Both factories were now employing 400 workers with room for expansion at Mold.

BELOW: No canteen here Emrys Williams(the profile) and Gomer Jones enjoy their butties.

ABOVE: The Esmor Works. Long low corrugated sheet buildings, cold in winter hot in summer.

ABOVE: Ready
to move. In the
background is the
Coles crane.

BELOW: Mk1V balers
coming down the
line.

ABOVE RIGHT: New
factory. Broncoed
Park Works Mold.

RIGHT: Just freshly
painted. David Jones
towing a Major baler
from the finishing
line.

BOTTOM RIGHT:
Boxed up.

LEFT: Machining
a baler gearbox
housing.

BELOW LEFT: Balers
for export.

BOTTOM: Almost
finished.

The Jones Royal Baler 1959-60

The Royal was a hybrid version of the 'Major' and Mk1V baler. Basically it was a Minor Mk1V but with the gearbox and drawbar of a Major. Was this a means of using up various spare major components.

This machine had a very short production run (less than one hundred built) and at the time of writing I know few have survived to preservation.

During the 1970s and 1980s there were constant adverts in the Farmers Weekly titled "Diesel Engines Wanted" Petters and Armstrong–Siddeley. An obvious source was the hundreds of balers in the UK. Balers were bought and scrapped whilst the engines were sold to the Middle and Far East for duties such as irrigation and marine use. This explains the scarcity of any engine powered make of baler having made it through to preservation.

BELOW: Royal. 1959-60. A Minor Mk1V with features taken from the Major.

BELOW RIGHT: Royal Brochure.

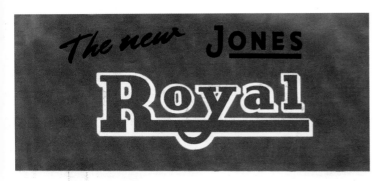

SPECIFICATION

The ROYAL equipped with P.T.O. drive

BOTTOM RIGHT: A blue Royal outside Bromfield Hall gates on Mold Denbigh road.

Jones Tedders and Hay Conditioners
(pto-driven)

The Jones "Tri-Action" Haymaker 1955–6

To quote "The Tri-action Rake serves three main purposes; hay tedding, side raking and swath spreading and will give excellent results in every operating position. The reel may be pivoted at any angle up to 45 degrees in either direction and the reel eccentric pivot is also adjustable to obtain a precise setting of tine "kick" to suit varying crops. The gentle but positive action of the machine ensures minimum loss of leaf and any lumps in the material are shredded out evenly and dropped on top of the swath for quick and adequate curing. The material can be baled considerably earlier and greener than normal methods because of the extremely even aeration obtained." The British farmer has never taken to multi-purpose machines as they were viewed as "jack of all trades and master of none". These machines were not a success and few were built. Priced at £135 in 1956.

This bold early attempt by Jones to modernise the difficult art of British haymaking with pto power continued with single purpose machines.

The Jones "Double Action" Two Row Tedder later '130'

Horse drawn land wheel driven tedders had been around for decades. Bamfords, Nicholson, Blackstone to name but a few had made thousands. With the coming of the tractor many were just converted for drawbar use. By the early 1950s farmers had experienced the advantages of the power-driven hay mower over land drive, they were soon to experience the benefit of the speedier power-driven tedder.

Most manufacturers used vee-belt drives, Jones was different using primary and secondary chain drives with a slip clutch for overload protection. This was later changed to vee-belts for the secondary drive. In 1957 it cost £166. The method of transport was protected by Patent No 831, 665, under the heading "Improvements in or relating to Hay Tedders".

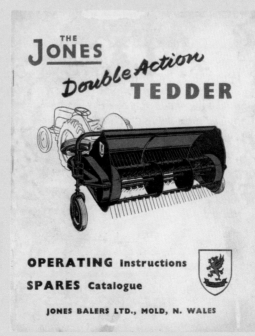

LEFT: This machine proved to be a problem when in the transport position and very few were made.

Using the machine

"Over the Top" when the swathes were green. "Kicking Action" a gentler motion as the hay was almost ready, to prevent loss of leaf.

Manufacturers saw a new market and Jones faced competition from several companies notably Blanch with their "Cock Pheasant." Under Allis-Chalmers it was designated Jones "Master Double Row Tedder".

ABOVE: Two Row Tedder advert 1956.

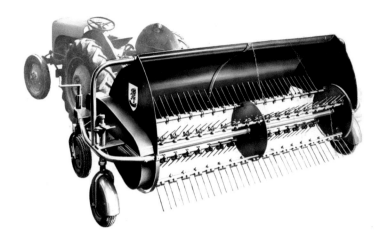

THE
Jones
Double Action
TEDDER
FOR TRACTOR P.T.O. DRIVE

The *only* successful way of making hay under British conditions!

This fine machine is designed for really efficient tedding with ease of transport in narrow lanes and gateways, and adequately meets the ever-increasing demand for an ' over the top ' Tedder. Driven from the tractor P.T.O. drive ensuring positive action in any weight of crop or bad ground conditions, the double-action mechanism allows the operator to gently aerate the hay by kicking under the back. The ' over the top ' action really turns the hay completely or kicks over the top according to the speed used on the reel. Further particulars will gladly be supplied by your usual Agent or you can write to us direct.

✳ *Contact your usual dealer without delay-supplies will be limited during the season!*

SOLE MANUFACTURERS **JONES BALERS LTD**

MOLD, NORTH WALES   Sales Department : Broncoed Park Works. Tel : Mold 70
Service & Spare Parts Department : Esmor Works, Rhoses

LEFT: 1958 David
Jones (Dei Tryc)
with Mr John Bellis
farmer of Y Foel
Rhosesmor.

LEFT: March 1960 "
Setting off for
Lancashire" A
consignment of 40
tedders leaving Mold
for Croft and Ewen
of Lancaster.

MUM
EUVRABILITY!

The drawbar can be changed in a
matter of minutes to the end towing
position for ease of transport through
narrow lanes and gateways, the
transport width then being 4 ft. 10 ins.
only.

. Tel : Halkyn 363. Grams : Jobalers, Mold

LEFT: Mr Maurice
Cragg unloaded the
tedders at Glasson
Dock.

The Jones Mini Tedder or Model 230

Introduced in 1958, priced at £125. It was really using the "Mini" name before the car or the skirt! A fast belt driven "Over the Top" action single row machine, for hay or for 'fluffing up" compressed or wet straw windrows prior to baling. Stiff competition from Bamford "Wuffler" and Bentall "Air-o-Tedder" and several others.

The Jones Forage Harvester 1956–58

During the mid 1950s the possibility of mechanising the silage crop became a step nearer to reality. The flail-type forage harvester with its cutting lacerating blowing action showed promise. Jones decided to investigate and built a handful of machines. Built on the in-line principle it bore similarities to the David Brown Hurricane. The Jones machine was ready for production but immediately there were over twenty other makes on the market. The only other Welsh forage harvester connection is the involvement of The Rustproof Metal Window Company (Saltney Engineering) importing Gehl double chop harvesters. They were also major suppliers of sheet metal components to Jones Balers.

RIGHT AND ABOVE:
Single Row Tedder.

The new JONES
MINI-TEDDER

‹4 JUL 1961

MODEL 230

RIGHT: Prototype
Jones forage
harvester. One
of only a handful
produced.

BELOW: John Wrench
of The Beeches
Farm Saltney with
probably "the only
one."

Over the top single action
POWER DRIVEN
GRASS SPREADER &
HAY TEDDER

LEAD WITH JONES

Every blade of grass will carry
its full protein value
provided the machine is used correctly.

Here are a few examples to bring back memories:
• *Silorator*
• *Lundell*
• *Wild-Thwaites*
• *David Brown "Hurricane"*
• *Blanch "Whirlwind"*
• *Martin–Markham*
• *Wilder "Sila-Mast"*
• *Bonser*
• *Massey-Ferguson*
• *Archie Kidd "Rotaflail"*

The Jones Manure Spreader 140

Price (1960) £215 Lifting Jack £2-15s-0d.
Jones were looking towards the move
to Broncoed knowing that they needed
more diversified products in their
portfolio. They entered the market
with their Manure Spreader 140.
By introducing a spreader in 1958 Jones
were almost ten years late into the
market. If I recall in our area of North
Wales many farmers bought their first
spreaders in the years 1949-1953.

By 1958 there would have been
very few first time buyers, perhaps
some of the early machines would
be ready for replacement. The 140
was a conventional "land-drive"
hard wood bed machine and would be
in competition with would you believe it
over twenty other manufacturers. Many
had options of either power-drive or
land-drive. Does the "Evenspreader"
pto and "Quickspreader" land-drive

from Salopian bring back memories?
Jones were experts at finding out who
supplied components to the other
manufacturers such as International
Harvester, Massey Ferguson etc. As
these parts were in volume production
Jones could buy batches at attractive
prices. Making spreaders would
at least avoid laying off workers
and keep things ticking over.

The 140 remained in production at Mold
under Allis-Chalmers up to about 1965, but
Jones had prototyped a pto model in 1960.

BELOW: Spreader
Manual.

BOTTOM: Dated 1959
as above on the road
at Broncoed Park
Works.

THIS PAGE: Wrexham
Road, Mold, outside
the Broncoed works.

Chapter 6

COMBINE HARVESTERS

**OPPOSITE: Pilot Mk2
at Rhosesmor.**

The Jones Combine Harvester

During the winter of 1955 the boys at Rhosesmor had been busy building the Jones combine harvester. According to the 2010 census of sales of combine harvesters in the UK currently run at about 600 machines. Today combine harvester manufacturing is mainly in the hands of the large companies such as John Deere, Claas, AGCO (Massey–Ferguson), CNH (New Holland). The smallest model will be 200 hp with a cutting width of at least 6 metres with a price tag of over £100,000. All will be self-propelled with large grain tanks. After the Second World War the UK combine harvester market was booming. In 1946 there were 4000 combines on British farms ten years later that figure was

an astounding 40,000. Competing for a share of this market were more than twelve manufacturers with over thirty models. In 1956 a farmer with say 30 acres of harvest could buy a 5ft 6in cut trailed pto-driven Allis-Chalmers All-Crop 60 for £535 or small 6ft self-propelled costing about £850. The contractor could buy the largest 12ft cut with say a 62 hp Diesel engine for £2,000-2,500. Combines ranged from trailed models to self-propelled with bagger and tanker options the choice seemed endless.

Manufacturers had not developed detachable cutting tables so country lanes and narrow gateways presented difficulties. Just as early balers many machines were of

RIGHT: Jones Pilot 5ft 6in cut combine prototype 1956. Left Glynne Jones, seated George Williams, Right Telford Brown (manager of North Wales Agricultural).

RIGHT: Aktiv M trailed combine.

Angetrieben wurde der Aktiv über eine Zapfwelle

SPECIFICATION

Overall height	– 8 feet 10 inches	Type of cleaner	– Scour cleaner with removable screens.
Overall length	– 17 feet 2 inches		
Overall width for transport	– 8 feet	Drive wheel size	– 750 x 16
Width of cut	– 8 feet	Steering wheel size	– 450 x 19
Width of drum	– 48 inches	Wheel track	– 7 feet 6 inches
Diameter of drum	– 17 inches	Wheel base	– 7 feet 6 inches
Speed of drum	– 800–1500 R.P.M.	Engine unit	– David Brown 34 h.p. T.V.O.
		Approximate output	– 2 tons per hour.

MAIN FEATURES

Header and thresher in line. Operating parts run by V belts. Precision balanced drum with six corrugated rasp bars. One piece straw-rack of all welded sheet steel. Riddle with adjustable tongues. Tubular chassis frame with tubular steel main axle. Twin drive-wheels fitted as standard. Ball and roller bearings for rotating shafts. Self-lubricating bearings for reciprocating spindles. Reliable safety clutches. Efficient earlifters. Low power requirement.

SOLE MANUFACTURERS

JONES BALERS LTD., MOLD, N. WALES.

SALES DEPARTMENT
BRONCOED PARK WORKS
Tel.: Mold 701

SERVICE & SPARE PARTS DEPARTMENT
ESMOR WORKS, RHOSESMOR, MOLD
Tel.: Halkyn 363   Telegrams: Jobalers, Mold

The makers reserve the right to alter, change, add or delete any material included in the specification of the machine herein without notice, also without incurring any liability to alter machines previously supplied

Temporary Leaflet — 250 235

Printed in England by Hugh Evans and Sons, Ltd., Liverpool

American origin and had a transport width in excess of 9ft. To quote for example the British built Allis All-Crop cut only 5ft 6in wide but had a transport width of 10ft 6in!! International Harvester (Doncaster built) B-64 9ft 6in wide!!

Most contractors bought the Kilmarnock built Massey Harris 726 with its 56 hp engine. This was the market leader but was too wide for country lanes. Massey would address this problem by producing the little 735 with its 23.5 hp Austin TVO engine. In the case of the 735 small also meant slow. In 1964 we had four acres of oats standing at over four foot tall. The little machine made heavy weather of the job with bits of straw mixed in the grain.

European manufacturers such as Claas, Claeys, Fahr developed small (narrow) self–propelled machines but were expensive and sold in low volumes. However these had reasonable work rates and could travel down the narrow lanes of the west

such as found in Devon and Wales. The British farmer had noted that the European machines excelled under damp conditions and with large volumes of straw. Unlike America straw in Britain had a high value and combines in the 50s and 60s were having to cope with tall crops unlike the short stiff straw of today.

British manufacturers such as Ransomes and David Brown entered the field by manufacturing well tried and tested machines under licence from Swedish companies.

Ransomes of Ipswich entered the self-propelled market in 1956 with the 12ft cut Model 902. In 1962 they brought out the smaller 8ft 6in cut 801. Ransomes would be the only British company to successfully change from making threshing machines to combine harvesters. They made their last "Cavalier" in 1976 thus ending production of a true British combine.

ABOVE: Pilot Specification.

It was now survival of the fittest. Many of the smaller European manufacturers ceased production, others kept going producing combines for the big companies (badge engineering). Others were swallowed by the multi-nationals.

During the 50s and 60s to have a combine harvester on their trade stand was the ambition of many agricultural machinery companies. It sent a message that you "had made it" as it were. A farmer would

buy the machine at a show stand to have displayed on it "Sold to Mr J Farmer" much to the envy of his neighbours.

It was sometime in 1955 that Jones Balers decided to add a combine to their portfolio. Jones were taking a huge gamble, their reputation was built on providing the contractor with fast reliable balers. If the combine was to succeed it would have to meet the highest expectations.

RIGHT: Pilot under test in a crop of oats, driver Harry Williams, bagging Bill Cooke. Note "Scour Kleen" grain cleaner.

RIGHT: "What do you think" Glynne and David discuss the Pilot.

The Jones Pilot Combine Harvester

The "Pilot "in prototype form was tested. The "Pilot" in reality was a self–propelled version of a 5ft cut Swedish built Aktiv Model M trailed combine. The Aktiv had gained an excellent reputation, coping with large volumes of straw and giving a clean grain sample. It had a good threshing drum width of 48in with a diameter of 17in. On the prototype Pilot the header was narrower than the rest of the machine so Jones fitted a 7ft 10in cutter bar with a short auger delivering the crop onto the canvas elevator. At the 1957 Royal Show the Jones Balers Pilot Combine Harvester was introduced Priced at £998 fitted with a 34 hp David Brown TVO engine.

Only about six machines were built. Its lack of success can be put down to the following:
Driving wheels were small 750 x 16, and it therefore lacked good traction.
Only a bagger model available.
With no diesel engine and low output 1 - 2 acres per hour it was also not a contractors machine.

By December 1957 the Pilot is quoted at £1295. None of these have survived to preservation.

BELOW: Pilot Cutaway.

BOTTOM LEFT: Pilot Mk 2. Cutting width increased to 8ft, twin wheels, fuel tank moved to improve weight distribution.

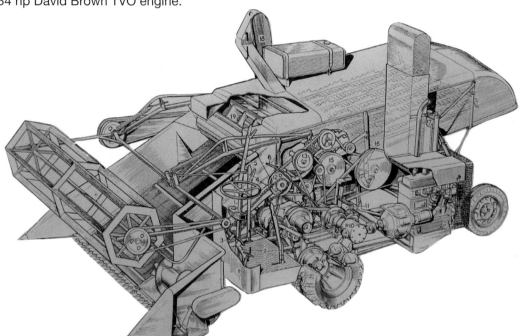

BELOW: Pilot at Pen-Bedw Nannerch. Left to right Glynne Jones, George Williams, on drivers seat Captain Nick Archdale with son Edward on his lap, Donald Mc Kintosh, Tecwyn (Llety).

THIS PAGE: Pilot Mk2
at Rhosesmor.

OPPOSITE: Pilot with
what appears to be
large driving wheels.

RIGHT: Pilot Mk2 in a crop of oats.

The Jones 710 Combine Harvester 1957–8

Based on the Aktiv the 710 had the David Brown VO engine mounted transversely behind the higher positioned driver. A few of these were made and were with an 7ft 6in full width normal cutter bar and centre feed auger and elevator and were the test bed for the "Cruiser". A 710 can be seen at the Greenfield Valley. This machine was new in 1958 to Lloyd Jones Brothers Contractors Llanfair DC near Ruthin Denbighshire.

RIGHT: The only survivor. The Cruiser 710 ex Lloyd Jones Brothers of Llanfair D.C. near Ruthin at Greenfield Valley Heritage Park Holywell.

The Jones Cruiser 810 1958-60

Introduced at the 1958 Smithfield Show with a drum width of 4ft and a cutting width of 7ft 8in and a transport width of only 9ft. For the 1959 harvest it had gained a diesel engine (Perkins L4); a larger diameter drum and hydraulic controls. It was also unique in that the threshing cylinder speed of 700-1500 rpm could be changed whilst on the move. Prices March 1959 Cruiser £1,500 this compares with the larger engined Massey-Ferguson 780 at £1775.

LEFT: Cruiser Model 810 7ft 8in cut.

BELOW: Cruiser 810 Specification.

BOTTOM LEFT: Off to the show 810 leaving Mold.

The new JONES CRUISER MODEL 810

7ft. 8ins. CUT SELF-PROPELLED COMBINE HARVESTER

MAIN FEATURES

1. Precision balanced drum with six removable corrugated rasp bars.
2. Drum speed variable whilst running.
3. Quick adjustable concave.
4. Four straw walkers 4' wide x 8' long.
5. Two adjustable and two round hole screened, size 3' x 3'4½"
6. Pick up Reel fitted as standard.
7. Channel chasis frame with tubular steel main axle.
8. Sealed Ball and Roller bearings.
9. Self lubricating bearings for reciprocating spindles.
10. Reliable safety clutches.
11. Efficient corn lifters.
12. Electric starting and lighting fitted as standard.
13. Hydraulics for platform lift, variable speed and Pick up Reel.
14. Tow bag chutes as standard.
15. 7' x 8" Cutter Bar, hydraulically adjustable from 2" to 2'6"

SPECIFICATION

Overall height	10 feet 6 inches	Type of cleaner	Scour cleaner with 4 removable screens
Overall length	21 feet	Drive wheel size	10 inches x 28 inches
Overall width for transport	8 feet	Rear wheel size	6.50 x 16
Width of cut	7 feet 8 inches	Wheel track	7 feet 6 inches
Width of drum	48 inches	Wheel base	9 feet 6 inches
Diameter of drum	18 inches	Approximate output	3 to 4 tons per hour
Speed of drum	800—1500 R.P.M. variable when running	Approximate weight	3 tons 5 cwts

SOLE MANUFACTURERS
JONES BALERS LTD., MOLD, N. WALES.
SALES DEPARTMENT **BRONCOED PARK WORKS** Tel.: Mold 701
SERVICE & SPARE PARTS DEPARTMENT **ESMOR WORKS, RHOSESMOR, MOLD** Tel.: Halkyn 363 Telegrams: Jobalers, Mold

The makers reserve the right to alter, change, add or delete any material included in the specification of the machine herein without notice, also without incurring any liability to alter machines previously supplied

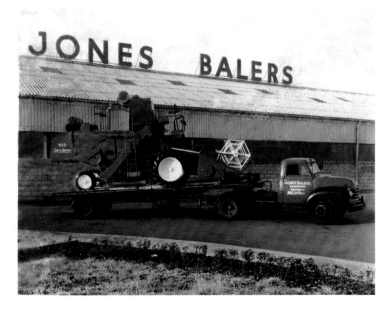

ABOVE: 1959 Testing an 810 at Jones Balers Farms Sealand. Standing Glynne Jones, driver Allan G Jones (son). Bagging is Merfyn Jones.

ABOVE: Final touches
for the show. Marie
Evans puts on "the
Dragon".

RIGHT: Night scene
Lord Mayors Show
London.

May 1960 New "Cruiser" Model D 810

Probably the first Jones machine that would not go through an 8ft gateway, it had an 8ft 6in cut and a transport width of 9ft. Jones fitted the American Hart "Scour Kleen" which had four cylindrical removable screens. This grain cleaner manufactured under licence by Rustproof at nearby Saltney featured on all Jones combines. It could sieve out poor grain (seconds) with a facility for bagging it up and providing a seed quality grain sample. The Cruiser had four straw walkers each a foot wide by eight feet long combined with a sieve area of 1440 square inches. In this department it exceeded the class leading Massey-Ferguson 780. These Jones' produced an excellent sample of grain.

1961

Jeff Ashworth of Skittam House Farm, Out Rawcliffe, Lancs as an owner/operator has fond memories of his Cruiser fitted with a Ford 4D diesel. "I found it a great machine that produced a clean sample of grain."

Price List 1 September 1960
Bagger with Cleaner	£2,250
Tanker with Cleaner	£2,290
Tanker less Cleaner	£2,250

LEFT: D810

BELOW: RDM 947 the first D810 tanker model. It is fitted with "Scour Kleen".

The Jones Cruiser combine.

The Jones Model 910

Very little known about it, since all testing took place at Sealand Manor Farm, their new large testing facility.

According to John Bumby (test engineer), "Our testing programmes were limited to the rather short UK harvest season. The big boys had the resources to ship prototypes to Australia so they could be testing in December and working the machine night and day. The 910 worked very well, mounting the engine to the rear of the grain tank solved eased some belt problems and also cut down engine noise levels. Had we brought this machine into production three years earlier things could have been different. This was the machine that contractors were looking for but the 1961 harvest was the last one under the Jones banner.

How many Combines did Jones make? It is estimated that around fifty machines were built.

Claas of Germany had introduced their "Matador" and Bamford Claeys the M103 and M8, even the top selling Kilmarnock built Massey Ferguson 780 and 735 were serious competition. In September 1961 Allis-Chalmers bought Jones Balers, and they wanted to promote their own machines the "Gleaner" EA and 5000 and so killed off the Jones combine. Jones machines under test now owned by Allis-Chalmers were dismantled. What a mistake!!

An Improvement on the Best!

This is indeed a fine machine, designed and constructed on a solid down-to-earth basis and at the same time reaching the highest possible degree of efficiency. Width of cut 8 feet 6 inches; approximate output 3 to 4 tons per hour; overall width for transport 9 feet. For fuller details and specification send to us for illustrated literature, or contact your usual dealer.

MANUFACTURED BY

JONES BALERS LTD   MOLD, NORTH WALES

Sales Dept: Tel. MOLD 561-701   Service and Spares: Tel. HALKYN 363.

The JONES 'CRUISER'
Model No. D 810 SELF-PROPELLED
COMBINE HARVESTER

ABOVE: D810 8ft 6in cut.

Chapter 7

STARS OF THE SHOW TO FINAL CURTAIN

THE JONES MANURE SPREADER

The Jones 'Super Star' and 'Star' Balers 1960-1968

Introduced at the beginning of October 1960 and were advertised as "The Stars of the Show" on Stand 124 at the Smithfield Show. These new machines were the product of two years of development. The design team were given a clean sheet to produce two machines that would result in Jones producing their finest balers. The Stars in all aspects out performed the Minor Mark1V. The Super Star re-established Jones as the best and fastest baler, and was possibly at it's best with the Ferguson 35 at full throttle. The "grooved bale" had proved to be one of the leading features of Jones Balers and so it continued on the new range.

RIGHT AND BELOW: 1960 The Super Star. Bales up to 15 bales per minute.

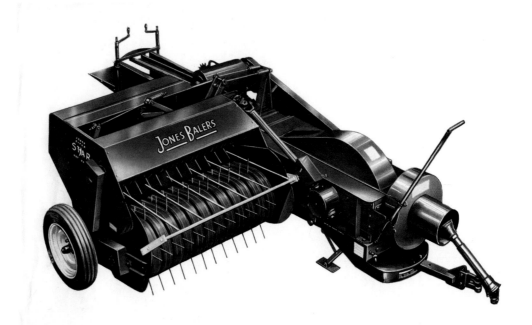

THE **JONES** SUPER STAR PICK-UP BALER

JONES BALERS LTD., BRONCOED PARK WORKS, MOLD, N. WALES
Telephone : Mold 701   Telegrams : Jobalers Mold

OPPOSITE: Only a picture. The name was changed to Super Star and painted blue.

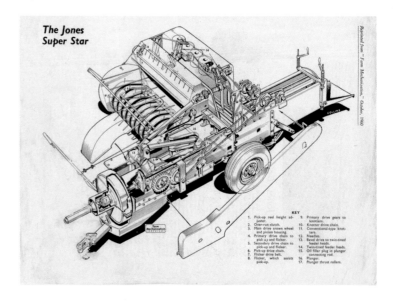

THE JONES
MARK VII

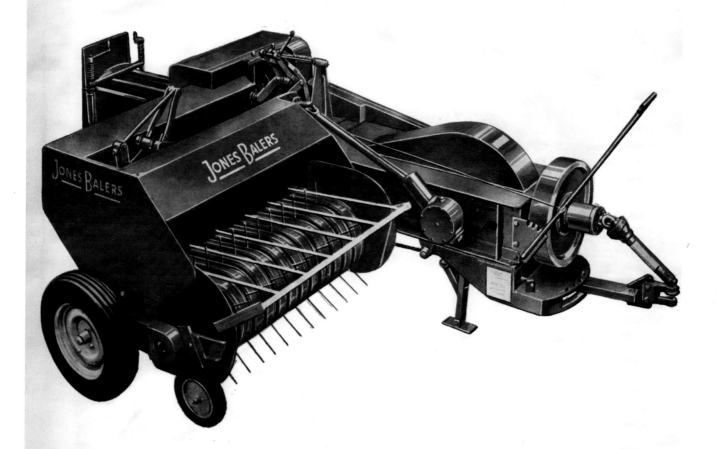

The new JONES
AUTOMATIC TWINE-TYING
PICK-UP BALER

1960 Production.

Changes for the better

The baling ram now ran on sealed bearings. This meant a reduction in power needed to drive the machine and better ram knife clearance maintained. On the old Mk1V the ferro-asbestos slides would wear out, so that ram to stationary knife clearance became excessive. A new cheaper knotter was fitted, built by Rasspe of Solingen in Germany.

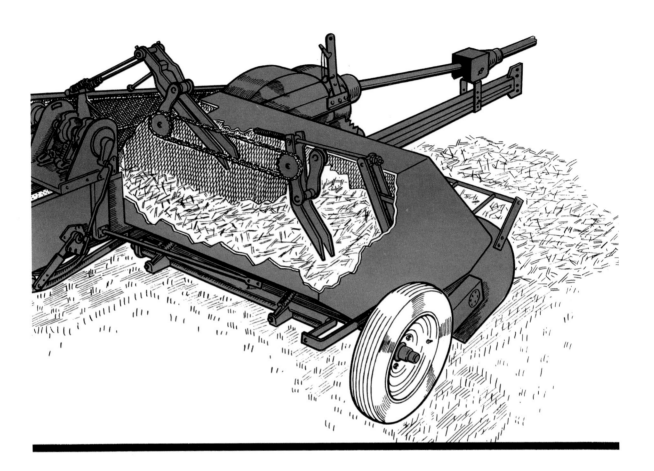

Bale length metering wheel

Sure-tie knotters

Bale weight control

Early deliveries were made by private plane to keep the production lines open.

This unit came ready set up to be fitted on the baler. In common with other balers the length of the bale was now controlled by a star wheel. Thus the "Jones Tucker Knotter" was consigned to history. A new feed system of transferring the crop into the baling chamber was developed and patented which really was the "Ace". The primary packer swept material collected by the pick-up reel to a second set which moved it into the chamber. This gave an even, almost continuous flow with little compaction of material near the ram knife resulting in further reduction in strain and power required. A "Top Feed Assistor", a favourite with contractors further improved speed of working and was available as an extra.

THE JONES STAR

JONES BALERS LTD., MOLD, N. WALES
A SUBSIDIARY OF ALLIS CHALMERS GREAT BRITAIN LIMITED

SALES & SERVICE DEPARTMENT
BRONCOED PARK WORKS
Telephone: Mold 701 (5 lines)

PARTS DEPARTMENT
ESMOR WORKS, RHOSESMOR, MOLD
Telephone: Halkyn 362 (3 lines)   Telegrams: Jobalers Mold

TOP: David Jones(Dei Truck) testing the Super Star.

ABOVE: Jones Star. Bales up to 6 bales per minute.

Jones also set the ram connecting rod at an angle so that it maintained pressure and thus clearance of the ram and stationary knives. The ram stop now fitted provided positive protection of the twine needles. Should the needles enter the chamber too soon or stay there too long the stop will engage the face of the ram and cause the shear bolt to break. With the increased use of sealed bearings, greasing and maintenance was reduced by half.

Price Super Star power-drive model £695 and with engine £895. It is interesting to note that as late as 1960 Jones are offering an engine powered option on the Super Star.

Price Star (power-drive model only) £605. The lightweight 'Star' at 22 cwt and more robust "Super Star" weighing 1 ton 9 cwt were a huge success and orders poured in. With these machines Jones had not only caught up with the competition, they were now ahead. Between 1960-8 upwards of 30,000 Super and Star balers left Broncoed Park Works Mold.

Many are still in use.

ABOVE: Jones Balers stand 1961.

RIGHT: A young Noel Jones with the Fordson Dexta and Star baler at Sealand.

BOTTOM: Prototype Star on test at Sealand.

JONES STAR

LIGHTWEIGHT HIGH-CAPACITY BALER

LEFT: Jones Star.
Bales up to 6 bales
per minute.

BELOW: Prototype
Star on test at
Sealand.

Allis-Chalmers

Allis-Chalmers of Milwaukee Wisconsin, USA was the parent company of Allis-Chalmers Great Britain Ltd. In 1950 they re-located from Totton Southampton to Essendine in Lincolnshire. Allis tractors and machinery always looked striking in their Persian orange with cream wheels.

In 1960 Essendine were about to finish production of the All-Crop 60 trailed combine and the Roto-Baler. The Roto-Baler had been in production in the USA since 1947 and at Essendine from 1953 onwards, by 1960 its sales had dropped to almost zero.

The All-Crop 60 built Essendine since 1951 was the victim of the swing towards self-propelled machines. This left two products the Gleaner EA combine and the newly introduced ED-40 tractor.

In Mold North Wales Jones Balers had started production of their 'Star' and 'Super Star' balers. It was reported that a "Super Star" had been delivered to Allis at Milwaukee for evaluation as early as March 1960. In the Farm Implement and Machinery

RIGHT: 1961 A change of name.

Review 1 October 1960 is an article under the heading British Balers for America. "Allis-Chalmers to make the Jones Super Star". Under the new agreement signed on 23 August, Allis were granted exclusive licence to manufacture use and sell the "Super Star" in the USA and Canada. Jones would receive royalties on the first 10,000 machines. The agreement was signed by Mr M Rhoten Managing Director of Allis-Chalmers, Great Britain Ltd and Mr Glynne Jones Chairman and Managing Director of Jones Balers. At a Press conference held at the Blossoms Hotel Chester, Mr Glynne Jones was at pains to refute the rumours that Jones Balers were about to be taken over by Allis-Chalmers.

Heading – "Jones Balers Factory at Mold will stay in production"
- "In the official release by Allis-Chalmers on Monday it was announced that Jones Balers, the firm started by two Rhosesmor farmer brothers less than twenty years ago, had been acquired by the US combine and would in future operate as a wholly-owned subsidiary".

The agreement was signed by Philip Bauer managing director of Allis-Chalmers International who before returning to the United States preferred to describe the deal as a "joining of hands". Mold had an assured future and its products complemented

RIGHT: The signing of
the manufacturing
agreement.
Left to right: Mr
JM Jones general
manager of Jones
Balers; Mr RD Tyson
company secretary
for Jones Balers:
Mr Glynne Jones,
managing director
seen signing for
Jones Balers; Mr
Myron Rhoten,
managing director
of Allis-Chalmers
(Great Britain) who
signed on behalf
of Allis-Chalmers
Maufacturing Co
U.S.A. DT Jones
director of Jones
Balers.
RIGHT: Phillip Bauer
Allis-Chalmers, right
Noel Jones, Jones
Balers.

FAR RIGHT: Allis-
Chalmers.

RIGHT: On taking
interest in Jones
Balers in 1960
production finished.

FAR RIGHT: The last
British built Allis-
Chalmers tractor.
1960-8

RIGHT: Changes.

LEFT: Jones Balers sells to Allis-Chalmers. September 1961.
Mr Wayman Hales Solicitor on behalf of Jones Balers receives cheque from Philip Bauer head of Allis Chalmers Milwaukee. Left Philip Bauer A–C, Fred Mayr A–C solicitor, Myron Rhoten A–C managing director, R.Derek Tyson company secretary Jones Balers.
Right representing Jones Balers Wayman Hales, Robert Jackson auditor, Mr Glynne Jones managing director, Mrs Glynne Jones director.

LEFT AND FAR LEFT: Made in England from 1964–1971.

LEFT: Blue becomes orange.

those at Essendine. The founder brothers Glyn and David Jones would now relinquish their association with the company. Mr John M Jones would remain as General Manager.

Allis-Chalmers had now bought both Jones Balers factories employing close on 400 workers. Broncoed Park the main manufacturing facility on an old colliery site of 13 acres was less than three years old. Esmor Works Rhosesmor (original works) a 3 acre site would continue some manufacturing, research, spares and servicing.

On the Allis-Chalmers takeover things did change

The red Jones Balers sign on the roof of Broncoed which lit up at night was replaced by Allis-Chalmers. A subsidiary of Allis-Chalmers appeared on all documentation and Persian Orange livery was to be the order of the day, the Welsh dragon was put to sleep and no longer featured on any future Allis/Jones products. As Allis had the Gleaner EA combine all un-sold stocks of Jones combines and most spares were scrapped. Thus the user of a Jones combine would soon run into difficulties. As far as the grassland farmer was concerned Allis was foreign and had turned out that "strange round baler". The market-farmers reacted and wanted a Jones Baler so more blue and red paint was ordered and Jones Balers and their Allis equivalents attained excellent sales.

The Jones/Allis Hay Conditioner (Crimper)

A machine not manufactured but probably imported from the USA (via Allis-Chalmers). Price (1964) £234. It worked by cracking the wax covering on the stem and leaf of the grass. The grass is passed between an upper rubber covered roller and a bottom steel fluted roller. The machine was discontinued 1965-66.

A farmer at Thurnham near Lancaster trialled the conditioner under good haymaking weather and stated that the hay having been crimped was ready for baling a day earlier than normal. Fully satisfied with the machine he paid the dealer John Jenkinson of Catforth. The next field was cut and crimped and but alas it rained, the crushed stems of grass deteriorated and the field was lost. The British weather and the mechanization of silage soon condemned the Yankee machine to the hedgerows of history.

LEFT: Smithfield Show circa 1968.

LEFT AND BELOW: Allis-Chalmers 5000 combine at rear of Esmor Works Rhosesmor.

FAR LEFT: Imported from America.

THE JONES HAY CONDITIONER

To return to the 'Super Star' and 'Star' balers

In 1963 various options were offered such as long drawbars, top feed assister. See Special or Optional Equipment. 1965 saw a facelift of the baler range with Jones "Star" Series 2/Allis-Chalmers "201". The styling was more modern, the long drawbar was now fitted as standard but the top feed assistor seems to have been dropped. The "Super Star" T and W/Allis-Chalmers '300 T came with a twine or wire tying option. Other improvements were larger diameter pick–up reels. By 1968 self-propelled combines of increasing size were producing ever increasing swath widths of relatively short straw. To meet this demand Allis brought out the Jones Mk10 T/A-C 505 T and W balers also the Heavy Duty Jones Mk12T/A-C 707 T and W.

These new models now had along drawbar giving four lateral positions and incorporating the latest in PTO joints so that tight corners could be easily turned. The pick-up reel was larger in all dimensions with more tines. The feed called "superflow" now had four cranks with the outer cranks operating faster than the timed packer head.

RIGHT: Drawings for horizontal crank baler.

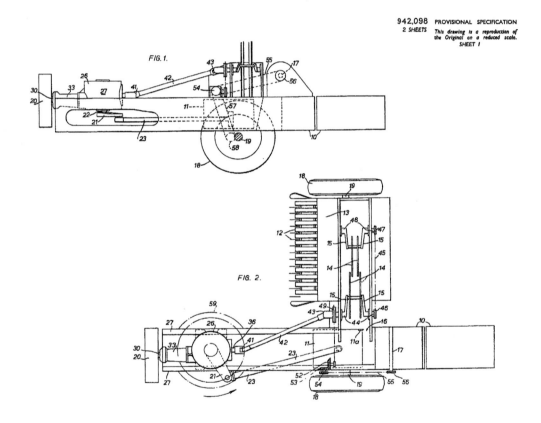

942,098   PROVISIONAL   SPECIFICATION
2 SHEETS   This drawing is a reproduction of
the Original on a reduced scale.
SHEET 1

RIGHT: Patent for horizontal crank baler.

942,098

PATENT SPECIFICATION
DRAWINGS ATTACHED   **942,098**
Inventors: DAVID THOMAS JONES and
GLYNNE JONES
Date of filing Complete Specification: Aug. 13, 1962.
Application Date: Sept. 1, 1961.   No. 31457/61.
Complete Specification Published: Nov. 20, 1963.
© Crown Copyright 1963.

Index at acceptance :—Classes B5, F (22B1, 23B1, 23C2, 23D1, 23G6, 23H1, 23L).
International Classification:—B 65 b.

COMPLETE SPECIFICATION
Improvements in or relating to Baling Apparatus

Allis-Chalmers now invested in a press shop under Noel Jones at Mold. In hindsight this would have been a logical step that Jones should have undertaken in 1959 but the factory move left insufficient funds to do so. The press shop enabled Allis to produce lighter better designed machines that could meet the ever increasing threat of New Holland. Prior to this the sides of the balers (chamber) had been made by Sankey at Wellington Salop, guards and lighter work came from Davies Brothers (Deeside Broadhurst) of Llangollen.

On the dealership front New Holland were constantly approaching Ford tractor agents who had hitherto been loyal to Jones. In 1964 the matter did not improve when the parent owners of New Holland (Sperry Rand Corporation) took control of Claeys the Belgian combine maker. Claeys were a major Ford Diesel customer!

Meanwhile at Essendine things were not going too well, the ED-40 tractor could not compete with Massey Ferguson, Ford and others and production of this model ceased in March 1969. Faced with competition from mainly Claas, Massey-Ferguson and New Holland sales of Allis-Chalmers combines were low. The Model 5000 made from 1968-71 did not take off and unsold machines were on the market for the 1972 harvest. Had Allis prematurely cancelled the superior Jones machine in 1961.

Essendine since 1960 had produced the wheeled loader and was now under pressure from America to promote construction machinery at the expense of farm machinery. In 1971 British Allis-Chalmers farm machinery interests and the Mold works were sold to Bamfords of Uttoxetter. The Esmor Works was sold to the ex-Jones Balers manager JM Jones and is now Tiger Tim firelighters. Essendine now becomes part of Fiat-Allis Construction.

TOP: Prototype horizontal crank baler at Rhosesmor circa 1961.

CENTRE AND BOTTOM: The clean lines of this machine that never went into production.

RIGHT: Shooting.

RIGHT: Farmer
Glynne in
retirement.

BELOW: The
Mk12/A–C 707 the
contractors choice.

BELOW CENTRE:
Mk10 an Allis
Chalmers
development.

BELOW RIGHT: The
Mk10/ A–C 505.

JONES BALERS
Mk 12 T & W
B A L E R

HEAVY DUTY

JONES BALERS

JONES BALERS
Mk 10 T & W
BALER

SERIES II

JONES BALERS

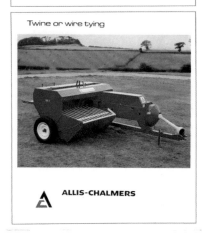

ALLIS-CHALMERS **505**
PICK-UP
BALER

Twine or wire tying

ALLIS-CHALMERS

JONES BALERS LIMITED

UTTOXETER : STAFFS. : ST14 8JD : ENGLAND
(Registered in England No. 516528)
Telephone: 3845 Uttoxeter (STD 088-93 3845) Telex: 36180

List No. JP.349/1977.
Printed in England

ABOVE: Bamford
days. Slurry
scrapers, tipping
trailers, grain drills.

BAMFORDS INTERNATIONAL LTD.,
UTTOXETER — STAFFORDSHIRE ST14 8JD — ENGLAND
Telephone. Uttoxeter (08893) 3151.   Telex. 36180

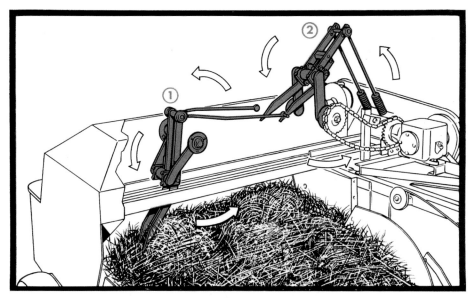

Rake No. 1 moves the hay towards the baling chamber.

Rake No. 2 overlaps, keeping the hay moving towards the chamber.

JONES MK.16
PICK·UP BALER

High capacity – modern design and engineering

JONES BALERS

JONES MK.16 BALER

The positive gear and shaft drive to the feed fork, packer fork and knotter units.

All illustrations in this brochure show the Mk.16 SUPER model.

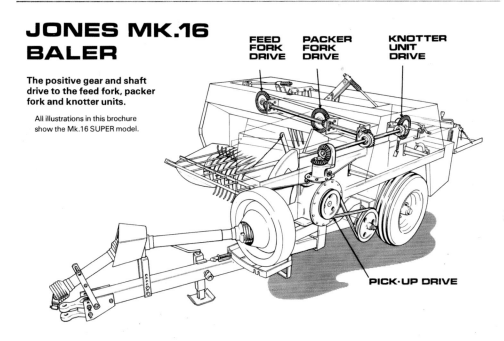

FEED
FORK
DRIVE

PACKER
FORK
DRIVE

KNOTTER
UNIT
DRIVE

PICK·UP DRIVE

Bamfords

Further reading Classic Tractor July 2007 "The rise and fall of Bamfords" by Chris Banbury. The origins of Bamford can be traced to the year 1845. Henry Bamford started an ironmongery business in Uttoxeter. His eldest son Samuel established the Leighton foundry and soon Bamford grinding mills, root slicers and chaff cutters found their way to thousands of farms both at home and abroad. The company were innovative and kept pace with the new demand for field machinery to accompany the tractor and had a moving line for mower assembly. It appears that around the 1950s Bamfords took the easy route of importing or manufacturing under licence. In 1954 Bamfords started making balers under licence to the Long Manufacturing of America. In 1959 Bamfords became the UK franchise for the Belgian built Claeys combine. In 1964 this franchise was lost due to the purchase of Claeys by New Holland. This scenario was to be repeated with BM-Volvo, Laverda and Kverneland. In the meantime the Uttoxeter range of machinery such as manure spreaders mowers and hay tedders were found lacking in design and reliability. The greatest opportunity to sort out Bamfords was probably missed when in 1966 JC Bamford put forward a proposed merger with JCB. This was turned down and a 41% share holding was acquired by Burgess. Frederick H Burgess with its head office in Stafford claimed to be the largest agricultural dealership in Europe, in England and Wales they had over eighty depots.

Bamfords buy Jones Balers (Mold)
In 1971 Bamfords celebrated their centenary and acquired the former Jones Balers factory at Mold from Allis-Chalmers GB Ltd plus rights to the Allis-Chalmers name worldwide except North America. This gave them licence to manufacture all Allis/Jones products, balers, combines, seed drills etc. Bamfords set up Jones Balers Limited at 16 Balance Street Uttoxetter and breathed new life into the Dragon to use it on both literature and machines. Mold continued to make the Jones Mk10/Allis-Chalmers 505 and the heavy-duty Jones Mk12/Allis-Chalmers

707 twine and wire-tying balers, as well as seed drills. The last of the slow selling Allis 5000 combines were built, probably to use up parts in stock. Bamfords used the Jones colours and name on the unsuccessful S4 and 245 forage harvester, and several other products including imported Jones-Laverda Combines, and Kuhn "Rotavators" and Welger big round balers (Jones Rollo). 1977 saw the introduction of the Jones Mk16 Pick-up-baler but with triple feeder forks.

Burgess now has control of Bamfords with a 61% shareholding and Hubert Burgess became chairman. An all shaft drive baler was introduced the Super based on the Jones 12T/A-C 707 priced at £3,125 and the Standard based on Jones MK 12/A-C 505 priced at £2,925. At a time when castings could be bought cheaper from abroad Bamfords in 1979 unwisely spent £600,000 on a new electric smelting foundry. Kverneland and Kuhn withdrew to set up their own operations resulting in the loss of a large proportion of sales.

By mid 1980 the firm crashed with debts estimated at £4.8 million. The liquidators created a new company Bamfords (1980) which took on about 300 of the 580 staff laid off. These were employed on work-in-progress and the supply of spares. The Jones Balers plant at Mold closed in 1981 with the loss of approximately 300 jobs. The ensuing sale at Mold of un-sold stock included balers, seed drills and beet harvesters.

Bamfords International Ltd 1981-1988
The assets of Bamfords (1980) were acquired by a consortium of Middle East investors led by Mohammed Zabadne and trading as Bamfords International. With a staff of 90 production of Bamfords/Jones balers resumed at part of the Bamfords factory in Uttoxetter.
Bamford BX3 baler for the small farmer.
Bamford BX5 baler based on Jones Mk16.
Bamford BX9 baler for contractor band large acreage.

1988-1991 Benson Group from Knighton Radnorshire (Powys) Mid-Wales

Acquired the assets of Bamford International with less than 70 staff still working at Uttoxetter.

Operations were later moved to Knighton, to all purposes the "Dragon" had returned home. Were any Jones balers again made in Wales??

Changing Times

The big round and square baler had arrived. Haymaking was in decline and silage making on the increase.

Wrapping of large bales had become mechanized.

Large tractors and tele-handlers, could easily handle large bales.
Farm buildings and "big bale feeding systems developed."
A well maintained baler has a long life.

Note

The horse fraternity and some farmers still prefer the "small bale" and every year on many a farm the "Jones Baler" makes the famous grooved bale and works just as well as when it was new.

BAMFORDS INTERNATIONAL LTD.,
UTTOXETER — STAFFORDSHIRE ST14 8JD — ENGLAND
Telephone. Uttoxeter (08893) 3151.   Telex. 36180

Brothers in Retirement

People of the calibre of David (DT) and Glynne Jones do not retire; they channel their energies into other projects. In 1961 on the sale of Jones Balers to Allis-Chalmers Glynne turned to his roots and became a farmer; his brother DT developing the North Wales Shooting School and later Flintshire Caravans at Queensferry.

The farming enterprise and shooting school are still based at Sealand Manor Farm with Glynne's descendants. The farm was bought in 1958 primarily to enable Jones to test their machines in relative secrecy,

be they balers, tedders and combines. For years they had tested on farms as near to the works as possible to the displeasure of some local contractors; but delighting many farmers who have only good memories of Jones balers and still feel part of the Jones families' experience. The land at Sealand was low lying with big flat fields. The soil being light and hungry, suited a barley beef unit in which Glynne took great pride.

David Jones passed away aged 76 in May 1984. Glynne died aged 74 in 1985 at a pheasant shoot.

Chapter 8

JONES BALERS (ENTHUSIASTS)

John G Bumby
– My Life at Jones Balers 1950-1964

RIGHT: John Archer
(Garstang).

Between 1950 and 1964 John worked at Rhosesmor mainly in the experimental department. I leave John to tell his story.

As a boy I would play truant from school to help with threshing and harvesting. George Denson of Penporchell Isaf Henllan near Denbigh, was a progressive farmer and threshing contractor. He was my mentor and introduced me to the world of machinery.

Denson was one of the numerous such contractors who were on friendly terms with "The Jones Brothers". On this particular day in 1949 Denson was re–testing a Jones Lion pick-up baler at Maes y Groes Henllan. If you recall many of these machines built by Blanch were faulty and came back up to North Wales to be sorted out. I was driving the Field Marshal tractor towing the baler when Glyn Jones arrived and enquired about the young tractor driver, "would he like an apprenticeship at the works". Thus began what was to be one of the best times of my life. On 18 June 1950 I reported at Esmor Works and became an indentured apprentice, clock number 108. Thus for the next five years I caught the train from Denbigh station to Rhydymwyn.

"Rhydymwyn" means the valley or stream of the mines, here during the Second World War was located a large munitions and Mustard Gas store. From Rhydymwyn it was an uphill one mile walk up to Jones', boy was I fit!

Part of my apprenticeship was spent at the Technical College at Wrexham. You were on trial for the first three months, I spent most of this time in the detail department with Cyril Mason and Joe Jones.
Rates of pay First Year 8d per hour (in old money) less than £1-10s per week.
Second Year 1s-1d per hour.
Third Year 1s-6d per hour.
Fourth Year 1s-1d per hour.
Fifth Year 2s-3d per hour. Wage of about £5 per week.
Minimum Agricultural Rate £4-19s-4d per week.

Much of this time I spent in the machine shop, turning the rollers for the rams of the Tiger and Cub. We had a small foundry but fortunately I was spared from this area. In June 1952 I was transferred to the "Experimental Department" to work under George S Williams.

The new Jones Minor had been announced but still needed testing and developing. I was given Minor No 3 pto and a New Fordson Major EIADKN TVO on trade plates and spent hours (all hours) baling. I had to keep accurate records of bales per acre, average weight of bales, mis-tying problems and so on. What a glorious job for a young man. Jones had a list of farms where we could bale and test machines. Farmers could be a "bit touchy" (short of patience) at harvest time, so some needed careful handling. This is understandable as the winter feeding of stock relied on good hay. Fortunately I have a good sense of humour in both Welsh and English as I "speak two spokes".

Much banter would take place, some farmers were better at rowing up, the majority had side rakes which tended to roll the hay into a rope and produce lumps on the corners. You soon learned to start baling a field a few rows in from the hedge as the rows near the hedge were thicker and probably greener. In those days there would be a few people in the field tidying the rows up, moving bales and so on. The Jones knotter was not the most reliable and baling loose bales you may know takes patience.

During harvest time there was plenty of tea in the "caddies", if there was no dew, baling until ten o'clock was normal.

Sometimes Glyn Jones would drop off one of the service vans for me to get home. Jones never queried the hours and I got paid accordingly. These long summer days compensated for the dark winter days spent drilling, welding and fitting at the works.

Assume Nothing

I was instructed to go to Mr Edward Jones' at Rhoslydan Bryn Eglwys Corwen to make modifications on a "Minor". I needed to drill a hole for a guard to be fitted so I plugged the drill in a socket and pulled the trigger. The drill was dead but a strange noise came from the back of the barn. I pulled again and still the noise. Mrs Jones came out of the house to explain that they were not on the mains but on a "Lister Start-o-Matic" generator. A light bulb was switched on and the strange noise turned into a steady beat, all was well I had power.

Without mobile phones and sat-nav finding a sometimes irate farmer in a field down a maze of Welsh lanes was a test of navigation.

Obeying Orders

George Williams and myself were on our way to a baler working near Nercwys. George said "turn left", I did so, "stop we've got the wrong field". I promptly put the Mk1 Land Rover in reverse and had gone back a foot when there was an almighty bang!! Looking in the mirror I was horrified to see

RIGHT: John Bumby
at Sealand testing
the first Jones D810
tanker model.
Note sack for
collecting second
quality grain and
weed seed.

the shape of David Jones' Humber 'Super Snipe'. George Williams leaped out of the Land Rover and gave the co-founder of Jones Balers a tongue-lashing for driving too close. Fortunately the Humber had a spring-loaded bumper and duly shot out back into place leaving no mark on the car.

Covering Up

We laid on a demonstration of machines for representatives of our agents in Australia. One of our servicemen got knocked out by the Baler needles tripping unexpectedly. Luckily none of our guests noticed. I moved the van and set it at an angle so as to obstruct their view, loaded the poor chap and took him to hospital. A few days later, bearing a few marks he was back at work and nothing was said!

Between July 1955 and August 1957 I did National Service, returning to Rhosesmor with clock No183. The works was now bursting at the seams with my department working on new projects to replace the early range.

Allis-Chalmers

When Allis took over things changed. I'd had direct contact with Glyn and David Jones for almost twelve years and been involved in their successful and sometimes not so successful projects. When no one else was around they always spoke to me in Welsh often starting with "drycha yma John" meaning look here John.

We "the Experimental Department" were now relegated to the second division and were given rather menial work. The big decisions were made at Milwaukee and Essendine. On the practical side Allis had just introduced the ED-40 tractor and soon these arrived at Mold and Rhosesmor. Up to now we had used mainly Fordsons and Fergusons (the market leaders). At 37 hp the ED-40 was a real step down we were used to the weight and power of a Super Major for testing the Super Star.

The Dexta had performed well with the Star and was our works tractor at Mold, it had a high road speed and used to deliver machines to the station. In December 1964 I finished work at Rhosesmor eventually becoming a Lecturer in Agricultural Machinery.

Our Jones Balers Adventures by Robert Archer

LEFT: John Archer (Garstang).

Brother John (Jack) and myself were the sons of Manor Farm, Nateby, Nr Garstang. In 1952 we borrowed £1,000 from father to buy a second hand Jones Lion Pick-up Baler. Re-payment was due with 2% interest. We bought a ton of baler twine from JA Crook of Preston for £80 and were charging 9d a bale in old money. At this time the Lion was the only baler with the speed and output needed for contract work. It had its own engine a David Brown VAK 25 hp (Vehicle Agricultural Kerosene) or to us TVO. Though a big lumbering machine it towed well and went easily down narrow lanes.

So we entered the world of baling contractors. We baled over 30,000 bales covered our own costs and paid father with interest baling our own at no charge. We used to reckon on nine strokes to the bale or about six bales weighing 65 lbs each per minute. It took two men with sturdy pitchforks to load them. With the Lion the tractor driver could not easily see if the baler was mis-tying so we often had a second person riding on the baler hand knotting any missed!!

The following winter we decided to convert the Lion to self–propelled or the "Archer version of the Invicta". As most of our baling was on flat land we estimated that the engine had enough power for the job. The conversion was to be of such that the baler could still be towed by a tractor and operate as pre-conversion. The driver would be seated so that he could see if the baler had missed, so doing away with the dangerous "baler rider". The bale density could be adjusted from the driver's seat. The machine would have good brakes.

An ex-army axle complete with diff and brakes as well as two commercial gearboxes from Murphy's of Preston were bought. Various chains sprockets and vee-pulleys and a bevel gearbox assembled. The project was a complete success with the vee-belts acting as a clutch and the potential of 16 forward gears. I also cured the mis-tying problem by observing the holding of the twine on a German Welger baler and adapting it for the Lion.

Lion No 2

It was 1954 and I saw a Lion advertised in Hertfordshire. We agreed on a price but had not solved the problem of transport. A friend of mine had just bought a David Brown Cropmaster Diesel and suggested that I took it to fetch baler. "It's fast comfy and has good lights" he said. Three nights later I arrived back with Lion. This baler also got the Archer conversion with the advantage of having a 30 hp David Brown Engine. Accidents happen and a metal tine entered one machine causing one of the large gear wheels to strip a few teeth. The man at Jones said they were sold as a pair at a price of £120, we had no choice.

Open all Hours

I remember setting out to fetch spares from Jones at about ten o'clock at night in the old Austin A40 van down the A59 Ormskirk, through the Mersey Tunnel and onwards to North Wales. On reaching somewhere near Northop I asked the way. My pronunciation of "Rhosesmor" was more like "Roseezmor". The man twigged and said "You mean Jones Balers?" and said that I was looking for some sheds on the right on the verge of a village on the side of a mountain. The man was spot on in his directions and John Rennie Jones the stores manager had the spares and paper work ready. I got home in the early hours knowing that there was no rest - more baling.

We bought two Jones Minor Mk2s one fitted with a Petter Diesel these made a smaller lighter bale than the Lion. This meant that we were making more bales which should have meant making more money. As more balers appeared competition drove down the price we could charge per bale so we did not gain much. Farmers preferred the Minor bale, one person could handle it. The Lions gave us almost a decade of trouble free service, paying for themselves over and over again but times change, the customer is always right.

Land drainage was all the go and we developed and built our own equipment, this meant that we had work all year.

During the early 60s we bought three new Jones Super Star Balers at £700 each from John Jenkinson of Catforth. If you recall we had paid £1,000 for a second hand Lion say ten years earlier! However our profit margins were about the same as more balers appeared the price per bale had dropped to 6d. The Super Star was a faultless machine

capable of baling up to 3,000 bales per day, we were counting bales in our sleep!

Robert Archer, Garstang, Lancashire

Jones Enthusiasts

See John Bumby. See John Archer.

Please visit hyperlink "http://www.jonesbalers.com/id3.html" and www.jonesbalers.com/id3.html

We would be delighted to hear from you.

An apology

So many of you are enthusiastic about Jones Balers I would have liked to include you all. Just because you are not mentioned does not mean that your contribution was not valued.

Harold Butler of Great Plumpton Nr Blackpool

Harold has rescued and restored a Lion and Minor. His Fordson Major and Jones baler combinations have won several awards.

Sam Evans OBE of Pennal Meirionethshire

Sam is best known for his restoration of his Jones Cub.

Noel Jones of Holywell (Son of Glynne)

Noel has put together a great collection of restored and unrestored Jones Balers machinery with only a few pieces missing from a complete jig saw.

Mike Lawrence of Isleport Farm, Highbridge, Somerset has probably the finest and most comprehensive collection of Jones Balers. These are featured in the DVD collection Isleport Hay and Harvest Working Part One and Two. The DVDs are superbly produced by Jonathan Eckardt.

Merfyn Jones of Corwen, N Wales hails from a family of threshing contractors and is the current chairman of Dyffryn Ial Vintage Machinery Club. Merfyn often displays the Jones Panther at working events.

TOP: Mike Lawrence with the beautifully restored Tiger at The Great Dorset.

CENTRE: Panther(Mike Lawrence).

BOTTOM: David Jones (Dei Tryc) standing by the Jones service van restored by Mike Lawrence.

TOP: Restoration project Lion.(Mike Lawrence).

CENTRE: Lion and Panther finished to a high standard.

BOTTOM: Sam Evans Pennal Nr Machynlleth adjusting the bale tension on his Cub

TOP: Sam explaining the cut off for the feed mechanism on the Cub.

CENTRE: I remember them well. Tudor Lewis.

BOTTOM: Dragon.

TOP: We made it. Noel – centre, David Jones–left, Sam Evans – right. Photo at Bryneglwys Show 1910.

CENTRE: Early Jones Panther circa 1948 (twine boxes not on chamber side). Owned by Merfyn Jones and David Humphreys.

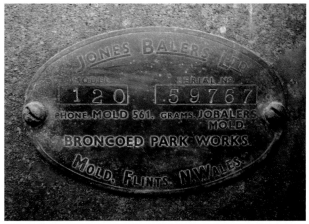

TOP: A 1959 Mk1V. Owner Haydn Morris Denbigh.

CENTRE: The only Jones Minor self-propelled baler. Restored by Mr Glyn Jones of Denbigh.

BOTTOM: The renowned Jones service.

CENTRE: Shown at Myerscough College Lancashire. Restored Jones Minor Mk2. Owner Harold Butler Weeton Nr Blackpool.

TOP: Makers plate off Mk1V first two digits 59 is year of manufacture.

BOTTOM: Sign of the times, the Jones Baler factory is now a business park.

Appendix 1 - Timeline

Machines built by Jones Brothers (Jones Balers) Esmor Works, Rhosesmor and Broncoed Park Works, Mold, Flints., North Wales

1942 First Jones "Tiger" High Density Self Feed Stationary Baler

1945 "Cub" High Density Self Feed Stationary Baler • Victory tractor Loader • Hammer and Roller Mills.

1946 Prototype "Lion" High Density Automatic Pick–Up Baler

1947-1948 "Lion" Model AC/T Automatic Pick-Up Baler • "Panther" Model SA/T Automatic Self–Tying Baler

1948 Jones Elevator Potato Digger

1949 "Invicta" Model SP/T Self – Propelled Automatic Self-Twine-Tying Pick-Up Hay and Straw Baler

1951–1952 The Jones "Minor" Model SF/T Pick–Up Baler

1953 Formation of Jones Balers Limited

1953–1958 The "Minor" Mk 2

1954 The SP "Minor" Self Propelled. "Major" Pick–Up Baler

1955–1956 The "Tri–Action" Haymaker • Hitches for Ferguson 20 tractor • Double–Action Tedder two row • The SP "Major" (only one produced)

1956-1957 The "Pilot" Combine Harvester • The Jones Forage Harvester (only a few made)

1957 The '710' Combine • Hitches for MF 35 and Dexta

1958 The New "Minor" Mk 4 Pick-Up Baler • New "Major" Baler • Manure Spreader • "Cruiser" 810 Combine Harvester • The Jones Mini Tedder

1959 Main production to Broncoed Park Works Mold • Jones "Royal" Baler • D810 Diesel Powered "Cruiser" (Perkins L4)

1960 Jones "Super Star" • Jones "Star" Balers • Jones Hay Conditioner

Appendix 1 - Timeline

Machines Produced by Allis-Chalmers at former Jones Balers Broncoed Park Works Mold

1961- 1971

Pick-up Balers
Jones Super Star / Allis-Chalmers 300.
Jones Star / Allis-Chalmers 200.
1965 Jones Super Star (Series 2) and Super Star T / Allis-Chalmers 300T.
Jones Star (Series 2) and Star T/– Allis-Chalmers 201 and 201T.
1969 Jones Mk 10/ Allis-Chalmers 505.
Jones Mk12 / Allis-Chalmers 707.

Hay Tedders
Jones "Mini" Tedder / Allis-Chalmers '111' Single Row Tedder.
Jones "Master" Double Row / Allis-Chalmers '222' Double Row Tedder.

Manure Spreaders
Jones 140 / Allis-Chalmers 140.

Hay Conditioner
Jones Hay Conditioner / Allis-Chalmers 500 Hay Conditioner.

Seed Drills
Allis-Chalmers 214 Seed Drill 21 row narrow spacing.
Allis-Chalmers '157' "All-Crop" Seed and Fertilizer Drill .

Combine Harvesters
Allis-Chalmers Model '5000' (small batch production)

* A batch of fertilizer drills were produced under contract for New Idea.

Appendix 1 - Timeline

Machines produced by Bamfords at former Jones Balers/Allis-Chalmers Broncoed Park Works Mold

1971-1981

Pick-up Balers
Jones 10T/Allis- Chalmers 505.
Jones Mk10/Allis Chalmers 707.
Jones Mk 16.

Seed Drills
Allis-Chalmers Model 214 Seed Drill.
Alllis–Chalmers Model 715 Seed and Fertilizer Drill.

Combine Harvesters (1971)
Allis-Chalmers 5000.

Other Jones Badged Machines (not made at Mold)
Jones/Kuhn Power Tillers.
Jones/Bamford 245 Forage Harvester.
Jones-Laverda Combines.
Jones Rollo/Welger Round Baler.

Appendix 2 - Price Lists

OFFICIAL PRICE LIST

1st January, 1956
(all previous lists cancelled)

"INVICTA" SELF PROPELLED AUTOMATIC SELF TWINE TYING HIGH DENSITY PICK-UP HAY AND STRAW BALER (V.O. Unit) £1608 0 0

"LION" MODEL AC/T AUTOMATIC PICK-UP BALER
Fitted with Diesel Engine Unit. Supplied on Pneumatics, fitted with brakes £1250 0 0
Fitted with V.O. Engine. Supplied on Pneumatics fitted with brakes £1147 0 0

"MINOR MODEL MK II AUTOMATIC PICK-UP BALER
Fitted with Petter AVA 2 Diesel Engine £875 0 0
Fitted with Petter PAV 4 19 b.h.p. Petrol Engine £865 0 0
Fitted with Jap 12 b.h.p. Petrol or P/P Engine £758 10 0
Fitted with Coventry Victor 12 b.h.p. £778 10 0
Fitted with Power Take Off drive and clutch £678 10 0

"PANTHER" MODEL SA/T SELF-TYING BALER
Mounted on Pneumatics and fitted with Brakes £698 15 0

"TIGER" MODEL BALER
Supplied on Pneumatics, or Steel Wheels, Fitted with Brakes, and including Four Dual Purpose Needles (for Wire and String Tying) £534 10 0

N.B.—In lieu of the Dual Purpose Needles we can fit the new type Collinsons One Man Operator String Needle at the same price.

"CUB" MODEL BALER
Supplied on Pneumatics, or Steel Wheels, fitted with Brakes, and including Four Dual Purpose Needles (for Wire and String Tying) £494 10 0

"MINOR" SELF PROPELLED AUTOMATIC TWINE TYING PICK-UP BALER
Fitted with Diesel Engine Unit £1125 0 0

NEEDLES
Set of 4 Dual Purpose Needles £12 0 0
Collinson's String Needles and attachments £9 0 0

JONES "TRI ACTION" HAYMAKER £135 0 0

HITCH FOR USE WITH FERGUSON TRACTOR £10 10 0

JONES BALERS LTD.

Esmor Works, Rhosesmor, North Wales.

'Phone : HALKYN 363 (5 lines).   Telegrams : " JOBALERS," MOLD.

OFFICIAL PRICE LIST

1st December, 1956

(all previous lists cancelled)

	£	s	d
" INVICTA " SELF PROPELLED AUTOMATIC SELF TWINE TYING HIGH DENSITY PICK-UP HAY AND STRAW BALER (V.O. Unit)	£1608	0	0
" LION " MODEL AC/T AUTOMATIC PICK-UP BALER			
Fitted with Diesel Engine Unit. Supplied on Pneumatics, fitted with brakes	£1250	0	0
Fitted with V.O. Engine. Supplied on Pneumatics, fitted with brakes	£1147	0	0
" MINOR " MODEL MK II AUTOMATIC PICK-UP BALER			
Fitted with Petter AVA 2 Diesel Engine	£850	0	0
Fitted with Petter PAV 4 19 b.h.p. Petrol Engine	£840	0	0
Fitted with Jap 12 b.h.p. Petrol or P/P Engine	£758	10	0
Fitted with Coventry Victor 12 b.h.p.	£778	10	0
Fitted with Power Take Off drive and clutch	£678	10	0
" PANTHER " MODEL SA/T SELF-TYING BALER			
Mounted on Pneumatics and fitted with Brakes	£698	15	0
" TIGER " MODEL BALER			
Supplied on Pneumatics, or Steel Wheels, fitted with Brakes, and including Four Dual Purpose Needles (for Wire and String Tying)	£534	10	0

N.B.—In lieu of the Dual Purpose Needles we can fit the new type Collinsons One Man Operator String Needle at the same price.

	£	s	d
" CUB " MODEL BALER			
Supplied on Pneumatics, or Steel Wheels, fitted with Brakes, and including Four Dual Purpose Needles (for Wire and String Tying)	£494	10	0
MAJOR MODEL MK V AUTOMATIC PICK-UP BALER			
Fitted with Armstrong Siddeley 20 BHP Diesel Engine	£898	0	0
JONES " TRI ACTION " HAYMAKER	£135	0	0
JONES TEDDER	£125	0	0

The Company reserves the right to alter prices without prior notice.   250-224

JONES BALERS LTD

Esmor Works, Rhosesmor, North Wales.

'Phone : HALKYN 363 (5 lines).   Telegrams : "JOBALERS," MOLD.

OFFICIAL PRICE LIST

1st December, 1957
(all previous lists cancelled)

"PILOT" SELF-PROPELLED COMBINE HARVESTER

Fitted with David Brown Petrol/Paraffin Engine and complete with Pick-up reel, electric
lights, electric starting **£1295 0 0**

"MAJOR" MODEL MK V AUTOMATIC PICK-UP BALER

Fitted with Armstrong Siddeley 22 b.h.p. Diesel Engine **£945 0 0**
Fitted with Tractor Power Take Off drive **£785 0 0**

"MINOR" MODEL MK II AUTOMATIC PICK-UP BALER

Fitted with Petter P.H. 2 15 b.h.p. Diesel Engine **£850 0 0**
Fitted with Petter P.A.V. 4 19 b.h.p. Petrol Engine **£840 0 0**
Fitted with Jap 12 b.h.p. Petrol or P/P Engine **£758 10 0**
Fitted with Power Take Off drive **£678 10 0**

JONES "TRI-ACTION" HAYMAKER **£175 0 0**

JONES "TEDDER" **£166 0 0**

OPTIONAL AND SPECIAL EQUIPMENT

Hitch for use with Ferguson and Fordson Dexta Tractor **£15 0 0**
Girling 10" brakes for Major or Minor MK II **£30 0 0**
600 x 16 Tyre and Tube when supplied with twin wheel equipment **£8 12 6**
650 x 16 Tyre and Tube when supplied with twin wheel equipment **£11 6 6**
Twin wheel equipment for Minor MK 2 and Major MK V Baler .... Price on application
Bale sledge Hitch Minor MK II and Major MK V Baler **£7 0 0**
Trailer hitch Minor MK II and Major MK V Baler **£15 0 0**

All machine prices quoted include delivery

The Company reserves the right to alter prices without prior notice.   250–250

Branch Works: Broncoed Park Works, Mold N. Wales 'Phone: MOLD 701
Sales—Phone: MOLD 701   Service & Spares—Phone: HALKYN 363

Trading terms as on 8th November 1957

Machines – HOME MARKET

Distributors discount on Mk 11, 111 and Major   = 25%   *25%*
        "   "   on Tedder, Tri-action ~~& Combine~~   = ~~25%~~ *25%*
                   COMBINE   = ~~15%~~ *20%*
Agents discount on Mk 11,111, Major, Tedder & Tri-action   = 20%
        "   "   on Combine   = 15%

Out of season discount to both distributors & agents :-

October	£45	November	£40	December	£35
January	£30	February	£25	March	£20

Machines – EXPORT

Price on application

Spares Discount – HOME MARKET

Distributors   = 33⅓% plus 5% cash settlement 30 days.

Agents   = 25% plus 5% cash settlement 30 days.

Repairers   = 15% plus 5% cash settlement 30 days.

Spares discount – EXPORT

Baltic Simplex   = 40%

All other Countries   = 33⅓% plus 5% settlement.

Discounts applicable to distributors

Minor Mk 11 Petter engine model	= £850. –. –.	less 25%	=	£637.	10.	–.
Minor Mk 11 J.A.P Engine model	= £758. 10. –.	less 25%	=	£568.	17.	6.
Minor Mk 11 P.T.O drive	= £678. 10. –.	less 25%	=	£508.	17.	6.
Major Mk V Engine model	= £945. –. –.	less 25%	=	£708.	15.	–.
Major Mk V P.T.O drive	= £785. –. –.	less 25%	=	£588.	15.	–.
Pilot Combine Harvester	= £1295. –. –.	less 20%	=	£1036.	–.	–.
Jones Tedder	= £166. –. –.	less 20%	=	£132.	16.	–.
Jones Tri-action	= £175. –. –.	less 20%	=	£140.	–.	–.

Discounts applicable to agents

Minor Mk 11 Petter Engine model = £850. —. —.   less 20%   = £680. —. —.

Minor Mk 11 J.A.P Engine model = £758. 10. —.   less 20%   = £606. 16. —.

Minor Mk 11 P.T.O drive = £678. 10. —.   less 20%   = £542. 16. —.

Major Mk V Engine model = £945. —. —.   less 20%   = £756. —. —.

Major Mk V P.T.O drive = 785. —. —.   less 20%   = £628. —. —.

Pilot Combine Harvester = £1295. —. —.   less 15%   = £1100.15. —.

Jones Tedder = £166. —. —.   less 20%   = £132. 16. —.

Jones Tri-action = £175. —. —.   less 20%   = £140. —. —.

EXPORT

Belgium — Minor Engine = £625. —. —. Nett
" P.T.O = £475. —. —. Nett

Holland = Minor Engine = £625. —. —. Nett
" P.T.O = £475. —. —. Nett

France = Minor Engine = £625. —. —. Nett
Minor P.T.O = £475. —. —. Nett

Switzerland = Minor Engine = £625. —. —. Nett

South Africa = Minor Engine = £645. —. —. incl. Delivery & Packing.
Minor P.T.O = £500. —. —. " " " "

New Zealand = Minor Engine = £593. 5. —. " " " "

Australia = Minor P.T.O = £453. —. —. " " " "
Minor Engine = £593. —. —. " " " "

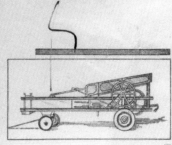

JONES BALERS LIMITED

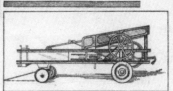

DIRECTORS: O. T. JONES   G. JONES
H. E. JONES   Z. JONES

MANUFACTURERS & ENGINEERS
BALER SPECIALISTS.

ESMOR WORKS, RHOSESMOR, MOLD.
N. WALES.

TELEPHONE Nº HALKYN 363 (FIVE LINES)
TELEGRAPHIC ADDRESS: "JOBALERS, MOLD"   OUR REF.   YOUR REF.
                                            RSB/ME

18th November 19   57

To: All Agents: Sales Policy 1957-58

                    1957-58 Prices effective 1st December 1957

Dear Sirs,

        Due to increased material and production costs, we have found
it necessary to make the following retail price amendments.

    Pilot Combine Harvester complete with pick-up reel, electric lights
    and starting   £1295. -. -.   Agents discount 15%

    Tri-action Haymaker £175. -. -.   Agents discount 20%

    Double action Tedder £166. -. -.   Agents discount 20%

        New price lists are now in print and will be circulated as
soon as possible.

                                Yours faithfully,
                                For and on behalf of
                                JONES BALERS LIMITED.

                                R. S. Bennett.
                                Sales Manager.

SALES

All communications to be addressed to the firm and not to any individual.

JONES BALERS LTD

Broncoed Park Works, Mold.

'Phone : Mold 701 (5 lines)   Telegrams : " JOBALERS," MOLD.

OFFICIAL PRICE LIST

1st September, 1960.
(all previous lists cancelled)

" MINOR " MODEL MK IV AUTOMATIC PICK-UP BALER

Fitted with Petter Diesel Engine	£840 0 0
Fitted with Tractor Power Take Off Drive	£655 0 0

" SUPER STAR " AUTOMATIC PICK-UP BALER

Fitted with Petter Diesel Engine	£895 0 0
Fitted with Tractor Power Take Off drive	£695 0 0

MANURE SPREADER " MODEL " 140

Fitted with Land Wheel Drive	£215 0 0
Lifting Jack	£2 15 0

" DOUBLE ACTION TEDDER " MODEL 130

Tractor Power Take Off drive	£173 0 0

" TEDDER " MODEL 230

Over-the-top Action, Power Driven, Grass Spreader & Hay Tedder	£125 0 0

NEW " CRUISER " D. 810 SELF-PROPELLED COMBINE HARVESTER 8' 6" cut

Fitted with Diesel Engine, Live Axle Drive, Independent Braking System and complete with Pick-up reel, electric lights, electric starting, hydraulic lifts to table and reel, also hydraulic variable speed

Tanker with Cleaner	£2290 0 0
Bagger with Cleaner, Tanker less Cleaner	£2250 0 0

OPTIONAL AND SPECIAL EQUIPMENT

Hitch for use with Ferguson & Fordson Dexta Tractor	£16 2 6
Twin wheel equipment for Mk IV	£23 9 9
Twin wheel equipment for Super Star	£23 9 9
Bale sledge hitch for Mk IV and Super Star	£7 10 6
Rotor Pick-up Land Wheel	£8 14 6

All machine prices quoted are ex works

The Company reserve the right to alter prices without prior notice

Spares : Esmor Works, Rhosesmor, Mold—'Phone Halkyn 363 (5 lines).

Service and Sales: Broncoed Park Works, Mold

250-454

Publication No. 1003/6

October, 1962

Retail Price Schedule

AVA
INDUSTRIAL

DIESEL ENGINES AVA
(Illustrated by Publication No. 3005)

Type					AVA1						AVA2		
B.h.p. (B.S. Rating)					3	4	5	6		6	8	10	12
Rev./min.					1000	1200	1500	1800*		1000	1200	1500	1800*

SPECIFICATION OF STANDARD ENGINE

PETTER type AVA four-stroke cycle, single/twin cylinder vertical air-cooled diesel engine, having clockwise rotation when looking on the flywheel. Engine complete with the following standard equipment: fuel tank, paper element fuel filter, pepper pot silencer, heavy duty paper element air cleaner, fuel pump rack protection, starting handle, operators handbook, tools, set of joints and gaskets for decarbonising engine.

ENGINE

	£ s. d.	£ s. d.
Bare engine (without pulley), Marks I, II and V	116 0 0	191 0 0

OPTIONAL EXTRAS

	£ s. d.	£ s. d.
High speed engine (1651/1800 rev./min.)*	7 7 0	7 7 0
Clutch (Mark III and IV engines)	27 10 0	27 10 0
Reverse rotation	No extra charge	
12 volt electric starting (less batteries)	47 6 0	47 6 0
SAE No. 5 bellhousing (gear end)	3 12 0	3 12 0
Variable speed governor (cable type)	4 18 0	4 18 0
Variable speed governor (ratchet type)	5 2 0	5 2 0
Oil pressure gauge	1 18 0	1 18 0
4-gallon fuel tank in lieu of standard	3 3 0	3 3 0
Extra heavy duty paper element air cleaner	2 4 6	2 4 6
Heavy duty paper element fuel filter	1 1 0	1 1 0
Pulley 5 in. dia. x 7 in. width	2 4 0	
Pulley 7 in. dia. x 7 in. width		2 13 6
Foundation bolts (set of 4)	13 0	13 0
1 year's recommended spares	13 3 6	20 9 0

Prices include delivery by goods train to customer's nearest railway station in Great Britain and are subject to our Conditions of Sale. Packing cases are charged at AVA1 £8 0s. 0d. and AVA2 £9 15s. 0d. nett, and will be credited upon return in good condition within 1 month, carriage paid.

PETTERS LIMITED

A MEMBER OF THE   HAWKER SIDDELEY GROUP

STAINES, MIDDLESEX

Telegrams: DIESEL, Staines, Telex

Printed in England

Telephone: STAINES 51333
Telex: 23871

THE JONES STAR AND SUPER STAR

PRODUCT PLANNING

4 JUL 1963

U. K.

STAR BALER. Short Drawbar with Bale Counter, Lifting Jack (P.T.O. Model)
Cat. No. 428   **£633 0 0**

SUPER STAR BALER. Short Drawbar, Bale Counter, Lifting Jack (P.T.O. Model)
Cat. No. 524   **£728 10 0**

OPTIONAL OR SPECIAL EQUIPMENT

STAR BALER fitted with Long Drawbar and Extended P.T.O. Shaft (Factory Substitution).
Cat. No. 429   **£637 10 0**

SUPER STAR BALER fitted with Long Drawbar and Extended P.T.O. Shaft (Factory Substitution).
Cat. No. 525   **£757 0 0**

STAR BALER Top Feed Assister (Factory Installation) ....   Cat. No. 1010—A **£20   3   5**
STAR BALER Top Feed Assister (Field Installation) ....   Cat. No. 1010—B **£32   6   9**

JONES BALERS LTD.

SALES & SERVICE DEPARTMENT
P.O. BOX 22,
STAMFORD,
LINCOLNSHIRE.
Telephone: **STAMFORD 2471**

PARTS DEPARTMENT

ESMOR WORKS, RHOSESMOR, MOLD

Telephone: **Halkyn 363** (3 lines)   Telegrams: **Gyrating Mold**

JONES BALERS LTD

Broncoed Park Works, Mold.

'Phone : Mold 701 (5 lines)   Telegrams : " JOBALERS," MOLD.

OFFICIAL PRICE LIST

1st September, 1960.
(all previous lists cancelled)

Please insert in your A.M.T.D.A. Folder

" MINOR " MODEL MK IV AUTOMATIC PICK-UP BALER

Fitted with Petter Diesel Engine	£840 0 0
Fitted with Tractor Power Take Off Drive	£655 0 0

" SUPER STAR " AUTOMATIC PICK-UP BALER

Fitted with Petter Diesel Engine	£895 0 0
Fitted with Tractor Power Take Off drive	£695 0 0

MANURE SPREADER " MODEL " 140

Fitted with Land Wheel Drive	£215 0 0
Lifting Jack	£2 15 0

" DOUBLE ACTION TEDDER " MODEL 130

Tractor Power Take Off drive	£173 0 0

" TEDDER " MODEL 230

Over-the-top Action, Power Driven, Grass Spreader & Hay Tedder	£125 0 0

NEW " CRUISER " D. 810 SELF-PROPELLED COMBINE HARVESTER 8' 6" cut

Fitted with Diesel Engine, Live Axle Drive, Independent Braking System and complete with Pick-up reel, electric lights, electric starting, hydraulic lifts to table and reel, also hydraulic variable speed

Tanker with Cleaner	£2290 0 0
Bagger with Cleaner, Tanker less Cleaner	£2250 0 0

OPTIONAL AND SPECIAL EQUIPMENT

Hitch for use with Ferguson & Fordson Dexta Tractor	£16 2 6
Twin wheel equipment for Mk IV	£23 9 9
Twin wheel equipment for Super Star	£23 9 9
Bale sledge hitch for Mk IV and Super Star	£7 10 6
Rotor Pick-up Land Wheel	£8 14 6

All machine prices quoted are ex works

The Company reserve the right to alter prices without prior notice

Spares : Esmor Works, Rhosesmor, Mold—'Phone Halkyn 363 (5 lines).

Service and Sales: Broncoed Park Works, Mold

250-454

Appendix 3 - Baler Specifications

SPECIFICATION OF
JONES BROS. CUB BALER
"CUB" MODEL.

FRAMEWORK AND DENSITY ADJUSTMENT.

Steel Channel Frame. Specifically designed for Tractor operation and maintaining a Baling capacity equal to a Bale per min.

The front of the Frame with a screw Gear to enable the size and weight of Bales to be adjusted to suit requirements.

GEARING.

Main Drive Shaft of suitable strength with 2 Steel Pinions with machine cut teeth, Mounted on 4 D.R.S.A. Ball-bearing Plummer Blocks, driving two Machine Cut Spur Wheels, specifically designed for silent and speedy running. Resulting in more Ramstrokes per minute.

FLYWHEEL.

36" diameter Flywheel, heavy, designed for easy running. Made of Cast Iron.

RAM.

The Ram is of Fabricated Mild Steel Construction with renewable fixed Steel Axles, and mounted on 4 Runner Wheels and Track cleaning Scraper running on renewable tracks.

FEEDER HEAD (NAGS HEAD).

Feeder Head of all Steel construction.

CONNECTING ROD.

The Connecting Rod is made of strong Steel structure, Big End fitted with Gun Metal Bush to give extra long life, the Small End being the fixed type.

ROAD WHEELS.

The Road Wheels are all Steel, convertible to Pneumatics. *Please state on your order type of* Brakes Extra (if required). *wheels required*

CONVEYOR.

Conveyor fitted with Automatic Trip Gear.

Trip Gear adjustable to make any length of Bale.

EQUIPMENT.

One Cranked Pressure Operating Handle and 4 Standard Dividing Needles.

Dual Purpose Needles suitable for wire or string—supplied at extra cost.

STANDARD MEASUREMENTS.

Overall Length 16'.

Height from ground to platform 5' 3".

Width 6' 8½".

Size of Baling Chamber 17" x 22" Full Size.

Length of actual Baling Chamber

Wheel Base 9'.

Approximate Weight 2 Tons.

PRICES : Carriage paid England and Wales ___ ___ ___ ___ ___ £ : :

MAKERS :
JONES BROS., Esmor Works, Rhosesmor, Mold, Flints., N. Wales
Telephone : Halkyn 248.

These Specifications are not binding and are subject to alteration without notice.

WILLIAM ELDER & SONS, LIMITED
BERWICK-ON-TWEED

SPECIFICATION OF
JONES BROS. "TIGER" BALER

(SHOWING ELEVATOR—SEPARATE UNIT)

FRAMEWORK AND DENSITY ADJUSTMENT.

Steel Channel Frame 5 x 2½ x 3/8, Specifically designed for Tractor operation and maintaining a Baling capacity equal to any other Baling Press.

The front of the Frame with a Screw Gear to enable the size and weight of Bales to be adjusted to suit requirements.

GEARING.

Main Drive Shaft is of 2¾ dia.; 2 Steel Pinions with machine cut teeth, Mounted on 4 D.R.S.A. Ball-bearing Plummer Blocks, driving to large Machine Moulded Spur Wheel, half shrouded, specifically designed for silent running.

FLYWHEEL.

Large diameter Flywheel, heavy, designed for easy running.

RAM.

The Ram is made heavy of Cast Iron with renewable fixed Steel Axles, and mounted on 4 Runner Wheels and fitted with removable Flexible Roller Bearings and Track cleaning Scrapers running on renewable tracks.

FEEDER HEAD.

Feeder Head of all Steel construction and mounted on 4 Ball-bearing Plummer Blocks and Races.

CONNECTING ROD.

The Connecting Rod is made heavy of solid drawn Tubing, fitted with large and small End Bearings, the small end being fixed type, and the large end is Gunmetal, bushed to give extra life.

ROAD WHEELS.

The Road Wheels are all Steel, convertible to Pneumatics.
Rear Wheels 8in. face x 36in. dia. (steel).
Front Wheels 6in x 27in (steel).
Brakes fitted (when available).

Please state on your order type of wheels required.

CONVEYOR.

Conveyor fitted with Automatic Trip Gear.
Trip Gear adjustable to make any length of Bale.

EQUIPMENT.

One Cranked Pressure Operating Handle and 4 Dual Purpose Needles suitable for wire or string—also 2 needling prongs.

ELEVATOR.

This is a separate unit and can be supplied separately. Made of all mild steel and supplied with a split pulley for fitment to a Tiger Model Baler only.

STANDARD MEASUREMENTS.

Overall Length 18ft.
Height from ground to platform 6ft. 3in.
Width 6ft 8in.
Size of Baling Chamber 17in. x 22in.
Length of actual Baling Chamber 8ft. 2in.
Wheel Base 11ft.
Approximate Weight 3 tons. 5 cwts.   N.B.—Measurements given do not include Elevator.

PRICES: Carriage paid England and Wales £   :   :   Less Elevator, £ 557 :   - :

MAKERS:

JONES BROS., Esmor House, Rhosesmor, Mold, Flints., N. Wales
Telephone: Halkyn 248.

These Specifications are not binding and are subject to alteration without notice.

Elevator £59. 10-0-extra

WILLIAM ELDER & SONS, LIMITED
BERWICK-ON-TWEED

SPECIFICATION
OF THE LION MODEL AC/T
AUTOMATIC PICK-UP BALER

MATERIALS & WORKMANSHIP	Only the finest Materials and Workmanship are allowed in the construction.
MAIN DRIVE SHAFT	Mounted on four 2¼in. D.R.S.A. Bearings equipped with one 42in. dia. Belt Pulley taking drive from Power Unit and one 36in. dia. Balance Wheel.
BEARINGS	Ball and Phosphor Bronze Bearings used throughout, for long trouble free life.
MAIN FRAME	Channel Section for rigidity suitably supported.
GEARING	Machine Cut designed for silent running.
RAM	All Steel. No Wheels, pivoting Type 30in. stroke.
FEEDER HEAD	3 Prongs operating radially and retracting at right angles to the Baling Chamber.
CON RODS	Steel Tubes, one each side of Ram to spur wheels.
HUBS	Front 5 Stud and rear 6 Stud Taper Roller Bearings.
BRAKES	Brakes fitted.
ROAD WHEELS	800 x 19 Rear; 600 x 15 Front. Steel Road Wheels provided if required.
WIDTH OF PICK-UP REEL	5ft. (Needle Rollers to all Bearings). Controlled from Tractor Seat by easily accessible Lever.
FEED	Directly from Pick-up Reel via Elevator to Feeder Head.
SLICER	Knives on Ram and Breast Plate.
BALE SIZE	Length—36in. Width—20in. Depth—16in.
DENSITY	Simple Screw on and off Pressure and Release.
WEIGHT OF BALE	Up to 85 lbs.
BALING SPEED	Recommended Main Drive Shaft Speed — 280 r.p.m. giving 40 ram strokes per minute.
OUTPUT	Up to 3 Bales per minute.
DIMENSIONS FOR SHIPPING	Length Overall … … 19ft. 9ins. Weight (approx.) 2 Tons 19 Cwt. Height Overall … … 7ft. 3ins. Wheel Base … … … … 10ft. 10ins. Width Overall … … 7ft. 9ins.

SOLE MAKERS :
JONES BROS., ESMOR WORKS, MOLD, N. WALES

Telephone : HALKYN 248.   Telegrams : JOBALERS, MOLD.

The Makers reserve the right to alter, change, add or delete any materials included in the specification of the machine described herein without notice, also without incurring any liability to alter Machines previously supplied.

Salopian Modern Press, Whitchurch, Shropshire, England

SPECIFICATION
OF THE PANTHER MODEL SA/T
AUTOMATIC SELF-TYING BALER

MATERIALS & WORKMANSHIP	Only the finest Materials and Workmanship are allowed in the construction.
MAIN DRIVE SHAFT	Mounted on four 2¼in. D.R.S.A. Bearings equipped with one 36in. dia. Belt Pulley for taking drive off Thresher Drum Pulley or Tractor
BEARINGS	Ball and Phosphor Bronze Bearings used throughout, for long trouble free life.
MAIN FRAME	Channel Section for rigidity suitably supported.
GEARING	Machine Cut designed for silent running.
RAM	All Steel. No Wheels, pivoting Type 30in. stroke.
FEEDER HEAD	3 Prongs operating radially and retracting at right angles to the Baling Chamber.
CON RODS	Steel Tubes, one each side of Ram to spur wheels.
HUBS	Front 5 Stud and rear 6 Stud Taper Roller Bearings.
BRAKES	Brakes fitted.
ROAD WHEELS	800 x 19 Rear; 600 x 15 Front. Steel Road Wheels provided if required.
FEED	Chain Conveyor.
SLICER	Knives on Ram and Breast Plate.
BALE SIZE	Length—36in. Width—20in. Depth—16in.
DENSITY	Simple Screw on and off Pressure and Release.
WEIGHT OF BALE	Up to 85 lbs.
BALING SPEED	Recommended Main Drive Shaft Speed — 280 r.p.m. giving 40 ram strokes per minute.
OUTPUT	Up to 3 Bales per minute.
DIMENSIONS FOR SHIPPING	Length Overall … … 18ft. 9ins. Wheel Base … … … … 10ft. 6ins Height Overall … … 7ft. 3ins. Weight (approx) 2 Tons 9cwt. Width Overall … … 7ft. 6ins. (Exclusive of Engine)

SOLE MAKERS :
JONES BROS., ESMOR WORKS, MOLD, N. WALES

Telephone : HALKYN 248.   Telegrams : JOBALERS, MOLD.

The Makers reserve the right to alter, change, add or delete any materials included in the specifications of the machine described herein without notice, also without incurring any liability to alter Machines previously supplied.

Salopian Modern Press, Whitchurch, Shropshire, England

It's the most compact baler ever built!

This illustration shows the Minor Mark II fitted with the Petter P.H.2. 15 B.H.P. Diesel Engine.

SPECIFICATION

Size of Bale	14" x 18"
Length of Bale	Adjustable from 20" to 36"
Weight of Bale	Up to 80 lbs.
Bales per Minute	Up to 6
Bale Counter	Automatic type fitted as standard.
Bale Slicer	Knife on Ram.
Bale Separation	Timed Needle Action.
Bale Length Control	Tucker Legs.
Baling Ram Speed	Up to 85 strokes per minute.
Tractor P.T.O. Speed	540 r.p.m.
Transmission	Totally enclosed Automotive type.
Pick-up	Spring Tined Cylinder.
Pick-up Width	52"
Wheel Equipment	600 x 16 pressed steel Well Base Rims.
Tyre Equipment	India 600 x 16 Ribbed Implement.
Hubs	Left side 5 Stud running on Taper Roller Bearings.
	Right side 3 Stud running on Taper Roller Bearings.
Standard Engine Unit	Petter PH2 15 B.H.P. Air Cooled Twin Cylinder Diesel.
Overall Width of Baler	7' 11"
" Length of Baler	16' 0"
" Height P.T.O. Model	4' 6"
" " Engine Model	6' 0"
Approx. Weight of Baler :	
P.T.O. Model	1 ton, 7 cwt.
Engine Model	1 ton, 12 cwt.
Shipping Dimensions :	
Packed in Wooden Case	15' 5" x 3' 7" x 4' 4"
Gross Weight, Engine Model	2 tons, 2 cwt.
" " P.T.O. Model	1 ton, 17 cwt.
EXTRA EQUIPMENT	Twin Wheels. Girling Brakes. Bale Sledge Hitch. Trailer Hitch. Hitch for use with Fordson Dexta or Ferguson Tractor.

SPECIFICATION
OF THE "INVICTA"
SELF-PROPELLED AUTOMATIC PICK-UP BALER

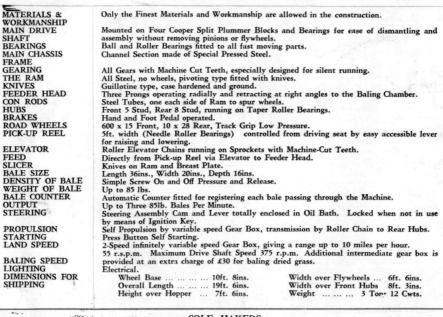

MATERIALS & WORKMANSHIP	Only the Finest Materials and Workmanship are allowed in the construction.
MAIN DRIVE SHAFT	Mounted on Four Cooper Split Plummer Blocks and Bearings for ease of dismantling and assembly without removing pinions or flywheels.
BEARINGS	Ball and Roller Bearings fitted to all fast moving parts.
MAIN CHASSIS FRAME	Channel Section made of Special Pressed Steel.
GEARING	All Gears with Machine Cut Teeth, especially designed for silent running.
THE RAM	All Steel, no wheels, pivoting type fitted with knives.
KNIVES	Guillotine type, case hardened and ground.
FEEDER HEAD	Three Prongs operating radially and retracting at right angles to the Baling Chamber.
CON RODS	Steel Tubes, one each side of Ram to spur wheels.
HUBS	Front 5 Stud, Rear 8 Stud, running on Taper Roller Bearings.
BRAKES	Hand and Foot Pedal operated.
ROAD WHEELS	600 x 15 Front, 10 x 28 Rear, Track Grip Low Pressure.
PICK-UP REEL	5ft. width (Needle Roller Bearings) controlled from driving seat by easy accessible lever for raising and lowering.
ELEVATOR	Roller Elevator Chains running on Sprockets with Machine-Cut Teeth.
FEED	Directly from Pick-up Reel via Elevator to Feeder Head.
SLICER	Knives on Ram and Breast Plate.
BALE SIZE	Length 36ins., Width 20ins., Depth 16ins.
DENSITY OF BALE	Simple Screw On and Off Pressure and Release.
WEIGHT OF BALE	Up to 85 lbs.
BALE COUNTER	Automatic Counter fitted for registering each bale passing through the Machine.
OUTPUT	Up to Three 85lb. Bales Per Minute.
STEERING	Steering Assembly Cam and Lever totally enclosed in Oil Bath. Locked when not in use by means of Ignition Key.
PROPULSION	Self Propulsion by variable speed Gear Box, transmission by Roller Chain to Rear Hubs.
STARTING	Press Button Self Starting.
LAND SPEED	2-Speed infinitely variable speed Gear Box, giving a range up to 10 miles per hour.
BALING SPEED	55 r.s.p.m. Maximum Drive Shaft Speed 375 r.p.m. Additional intermediate gear box is provided at an extra charge of £30 for baling dried grass.
LIGHTING	Electrical.

DIMENSIONS FOR SHIPPING

Wheel Base	10ft. 8ins.	Width over Flywheels	6ft. 6ins.
Overall Length	19ft. 6ins.	Width over Front Hubs	8ft. 3ins.
Height over Hopper	7ft. 6ins.	Weight	3 Tons 12 Cwts.

SOLE MAKERS :
JONES BROS., ESMOR WORKS, MOLD, N. WALES

Telephone : HALKYN 248.   Telegrams : JOBALERS, MOLD.

The Makers reserve the right to alter, change, add or delete any materials included in the specifications of the machine described herein without notice, also without incurring any liability to alter Machines previously supplied.

Salopian Modern Press, Whitchurch, Shropshire, England

It's a NEW STREAMLINED WINNER whichever way you look at it . . . . .

★ Never before has the *MINOR* incorporated so many remarkable worthwhile features to give fast clean low cost baling of high quality hay!

★ The many features have got to be seen to be appreciated—but here are just a few to set you thinking :—

★ The new *MINOR MARK IV* is compact, economical, efficient. Has a gentle leaf action, operates with complete safety and produces well formed and firm bales. Full floating pick up, adjustable hitch and a new shorter length for greater manoeuvrability.

MINOR SPECIFICATION

Size of Bale	— 14 inches x 18 inches		Wheel equipment	— 600 X 16" Pressed steel with based rims
Length of Bale	— Adjustable from 20 inches to 36 inches		Tyre equipment	— India 600 x 16" Ribbed Implement
Weight of Bale	— Up to 60 lb.		Hubs	— Right 3 stud, Left 5 Stud, running on paper roller bearings
Bales per minute	— Up to 6			
Bale Counter	— Automatic			
Bale Slicer	— Knife on Ram		Tow Bar	— Adjustable radially and telescopically
Bale Separation	— Timed Needle Action			
Bale Length Control	— Tucker Legs		P.T.O. Shaft	— Fitted with safety covers Standard 1¾" spline Optional 1⅛" spline
Baling Ram Speed	— Up to 85 strokes per minute			
Tractor PTO Speed	— 540 R.P.M.		Width of Baler	— 7 ft. 10 inches
Transmission	— Totally enclosed automotive type		Length of Baler	— Overall Length 14' 9"
			Height	— 4 ft. 6 inches
Pick Up Width	— 52 inches		Weight	— I ton 7 cwts.

The Famous Grooved Bale

Due to the unique chamber design, each Minor Bale is recessed for the twine. It is virtually impossible for the twine to slip off a Jones Bale ; a marked saving in twine is shown as compared with other methods ; the grooves also assist in aerating stacked bales.

SOLE MANUFACTURERS

JONES BALERS LTD., MOLD, N. WALES

SALES DEPARTMENT
BRONCOED PARK WORKS
Tel.: Mold 701

SERVICE & SPARE PARTS DEPARTMENT
ESMOR WORKS, RHOSESMOR, MOLD
Tel.: Halkyn 363   Telegrams: Jobalers Mold

The makers reserve the right to alter, change, add or delete any material included in the specification of the machine herein without notice, also without incurring any liability to alter machines previously supplied.

250—285   *Temporary Leaflet*   *Printed in England by Hugh Evans and Sons, Ltd., Liverpool*

Specification for Super Star

Bale Section	—	14 inches x 18 inches. (36 cm. x 46 cm.)
Length of Bale	—	Adjustable from 12 inches to 42 inches. (30 cm. to 108 cm.)
Weight of Bale	—	Up to 80 lbs. (36·29 klgs.)
Bale Counter	—	Automatic counter fitted.
Bale Slicer	—	Knife on Ram.
Bale Separation	—	Timed Needle Action.
Bale length control	—	Starwheel
Baling Ram Speed	—	Up to 85 strokes per minute.
Tractor P.T.O. Speed	—	540 r.p.m. minimum. 660 r.p.m. maximum.
Transmission	—	Totally enclosed automative type.
Pick up width	—	57 inches. (145 cm.) Flared to 60″ (152 cm.)
Tyre Equipment	—	640 x 15 inches Ribbed Implement. L.H. 500 x 15 „ „ „ R.H.
Tow Bar	—	Adjustable radially and telescopically.
Width of Baler	—	8 ft.
Length of Baler	—	Overall length 14 ft. 6 inches.
Height overall	—	4 ft. 10 inches P.T.O. 6 ft. 0 inches Engine.
Weight	—	P.T.O. Model 3192 lbs. Engine Model 3416 lbs.

EXTRA EQUIPMENT
Bale Sledge Hitch.
Trailer Hitch.
Rotor Land Wheel.
Hitch for certain tractors not fitted with an A.S.A.E Drawbar.
Long Drawbar.
9·00 x 16 L/H Wheel conversion.

Engine. For information regarding the maintenance, etc. of the Petter engine, refer to the Engine Manual supplied with the Engine Model Baler.

The makers reserve the right to alter, change, add or delete any material included in the specification of the machine herein without notice, also without incurring any liability to alter machines previously supplied.

The highest output BALER yet manufactured

producing the world famous grooved bale – length and weight adjustable to your convenience.

SPECIFICATION OF SUPER-STAR

Size of Bale	14" x 18" (35.5 cm. x 45.5 cm)	Tyre Equipment	600 x 16 Ribbed Implement.
Length of Bale	Adjustable from 20" to 36" (50 cm to 90 cm)	Hubs	Left side 5 stud Right side 3 Stud
Weight of Bale	Up to 80 lbs. (36.287 Kilos)	OVERALL :	
Bales per Minute	Up to 12	Width	8 feet
Bale Counter	Automatic type fitted as standard	Length	14 feet
Bale Slicer	Knife on Ram	Height	4 feet 6 inches
Bale Separation	Timed Needle Action	Approx. Weight of Baler :	
Bale Length Control	Starwheel	P.T.O. Model	I ton, 9 cwt
Tying Mechanism	Simple conventional Knotter	Engine Model	I ton, 13 cwt
Baling Ram Speed	Up to 85 strokes per minute		
Tractor P.T.O. Speed	540 r.p.m. minimum		Rotor Land Wheel
Transmission	Totally enclosed Automatic type		Twin Wheels
Pick-up	Spring Tined Cylinder	EXTRA EQUIPMENT	Girling Brakes
Pick-up Width	56½"		Bale Sledge Hitch
Wheel Equipment	600 x 16 pressed steel Well Base Rims		Trailer Hitch
			Hitch for use with Fordson Dexta or Ferguson Tractor

Due to the unique chamber design, each Bale is recessed for the twine. It is virtually impossible for the twine to slip off a Jones Bale ; a marked saving in twine is shown as compared with other methods ; the grooves also assist in aerating stacked bales.

Sole Manufacturers **JONES BALERS LTD, MOLD N. WALES**
PIONEERS OF BRITISH AUTOMATIC SELF-TYING BALERS

SALES and SERVICE
BRONCOED PARK WORKS
Telephone: MOLD 701 (5 Lines)

SPARE PARTS DEPARTMENT
ESMOR WORKS, RHOSESMOR, MOLD
Telephone: HALKYN 363 (3 Lines)   Telegrams: JOBALERS, MOLD

The makers reserve the right to alter, change, add or delete any material included in the specification of the machine herein without notice, also without incurring any liability to alter machines previously supplied

Printed in England by Hugh Evans and Sons, Ltd., Liverpool

Exclusive to Jones Balers is the Grooved Bale which saves a considerable amount of Twine per Bale. It is virtually impossible for the Twine to slip out of the Grooves and additional aeration in the stack is also achieved by the grooves.

SPECIFICATION

Size of Bale	— 14 inches x 18 inches (35.5 cm. x 45.5 cm.)
Length of Bale	— Adjustable from 20 inches to 36 inches (50cm to 90cm)
Weight of Bale	— Up to 80 lbs. (36.287 Kilos)
Bales per minute	— Up to 6
Bale Counter	— Automatic type fitted as standard
Bale Slicer	— Knife on Ram
Bale Separation	— Timed Needle Action
Bale Length Control	— Starwheel
Tying Mechanism	— Simple conventional Knotter
Ram con-rod	— Sealed for life bearing on big-end.
Baling Ram Speed	— Up to 85 strokes per minute
Tractor P.T.O. Speed	— 540 r.p.m. minimum
Transmission	— Totally enclosed automotive type
Pick-up	— Spring Tined Cylinder
Pick-up Width	— 52 inches
Hubs	— 3 Stud Taper Roller Bearing
Wheel Equipment	— 3 stud pressed steel well base rims
Tyre Equipment	— 5.50 x 16 Ribbed Implement

OVERALL :

Width	— 7 foot 10 inches
Length	— Working 14 feet. Storing and Transport 11 feet 4 inches
Height	— 4 feet 6 inches

Approximate weight of Baler — 22 cwt.

OPTIONAL EXTRAS

Hitch for use with Fordson Dexta or Ferguson Tractor.

Sole Manufacturers **JONES BALERS LTD, MOLD N. WALES**
PIONEERS OF BRITISH AUTOMATIC SELF-TYING BALERS

SALES and SERVICE
BRONCOED PARK WORKS
Telephone: MOLD 701 (5 Lines)

SPARE PARTS DEPARTMENT
ESMOR WORKS, RHOSESMOR, MOLD
Telephone: HALKYN 363 (3 Lines)   Telegrams: JOBALERS, MOLD

The makers reserve the right to alter, change, add or delete any material included in the specification of the machine herein without notice, also without incurring any liability to alter machines previously supplied

PART NO. 250—459

Printed in England by Hugh Evans and Sons, Ltd., Liverpool

Appendix 4 - Baler Secifications

Early days
Charles H Williams Glaslyn Foundry Porthmadog-gears.
Jones and Jones Flint foundry
Jonathan Collinson Garstang-baler needles.

Davies Brothers (Deeside Broadhurst) Llangollen - Sheet metal, pressings, guards.
Hardy Spicer Ltd Birmingham - Power drive shafts and universal joints.
Rustproof Metal Window and Engineering Co. Ltd. Saltney, Chester - combine harvester sieves, augers.
Ferodo Chapel-en-le-Frith - drive belts, brakes.
India Tyre and Rubber Co
English Numbering Machines Enfield - bale counters.
J.Sankey and Sons Wellington - baler chamber pressings, wheels.
British Timken Ltd Duston - bearings.
Hoffmann Chelmsford - bearings.
Skefko Ball Bearing Co Luton
Moss Gear Co Ltd Birmingham -gears.
Warwills Abertillery - castings
Penney and Porter Ltd Lincoln - combine rotary screens.
W.A.Tyzack and Sons Sheffield - baler, combine knives.
Renold Chains Manchester - roller chain.
William Reynolds and Sons (Bedford) - pick-up reel for combine.
Regent Axle Co Burnley - axles.

Engines
Armstrong Siddeley Motors, Hucclecote.
Enfield Industrial Engines, Reddich.
David Brown Corporation, Meltham.
Turner Manufacturing, Wolverhampton.
Coventry Victor Motor Co, Coventry.
Ford Motor Co, Dagenham.
Morris Motors, Cowley.
F. PerkinsLtd, Peterborough.
J.A.Prestwich, London.
Petters Ltd, Staines.

Appendix 5 - Estimated Production

	Tiger	Cub	Lion	Panther	Invicta	Minor	Star/Sup Star	Totals
1942	4							4
1943	12							12
1944	25							25
1945	50	10						60
1946	80	40	1					121
1947	90	130	8					228
1948	120	140	30	3				293
1949	55	190	150	50	3			448
1950	40	145	165	105	10			465
1951	40	120	180	200	25	4		569
1952	20	55	200	225	30	50		580
1953	10	40	180	90	20	250		590
1954	5	10	50	50	10	475		600
1955						900		900
1956						1050		1050
1957						1100		1100
1958						1150		1150
1959						1200	5	1205
1960						600	800	1400
1961							2600	2600
Totals	551	880	964	723	98	6779	3405	13400

Appendix 6 - Adverts

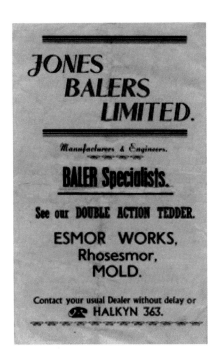

JONES BALERS LTD

have pleasure in announcing
details of their Advertising Campaign
for the 1957-8 season

*

JONES BALERS LTD., MOLD, NORTH WALES
Telephone: HALKYN 363

These advertisements are booked to appear regularly from OCT. 1957 to SEPT. 1958 in the following journals :-

FARMERS WEEKLY

FARMER & STOCKBREEDER

DAIRY FARMER

FARMING NEWS (Scotland)

ULSTER FARMERS JOURNAL

IRISH FARMERS JOURNAL

FARM MECHANIZATION

FARM IMPLEMENT REVIEW

AGRICULTURAL MACHINERY JOURNAL

and will cover most special Show Numbers.

JONES BALERS *mean Business!*

-Yes! it's Publicity with a PUNCH - designed to SELL...

The illustrations above, and those on far right are reproductions in miniature of our publicity agent's original advertisement layouts. A finished full size advertisement is shown on the centre page.

The Products of JONES BALERS
have a pedigree too...

Quality in design, material and construction has been apparent in every machine produced by Jones Balers Ltd., and today, the famous Jones Minor Mark IV is a typical example of a 'pedigree' product from a specialist in the manufacture of farm machinery.

The minimum of moving parts and compact design have provided the farmer with a trouble-free 'go-anywhere' baler, easily handled under the most exacting conditions. See your agent today!

JONES Minor MARK IV. BALER

THE JONES "CRUISER" COMBINE HARVESTER

THE JONES "DOUBLE-ACTION" TEDDER

THE JONES MANURE SPREADER

Manufactured by:—

JONES BALERS LTD., Mold, North Wales

Sales Dept.: Tel MOLD 561-701   Service and Spares: Tel HALKYN 363 (5 lines)

THE
JONES
Double Action
TEDDER
FOR TRACTOR P.T.O. DRIVE

The *only* successful way of making hay under British conditions!

This fine machine is designed for really efficient tedding with ease of transport in narrow lanes and gateways, and adequately meets the ever-increasing demand for an ' over the top ' Tedder. Driven from the tractor P.T.O. drive ensuring positive action in any weight of crop or bad ground conditions, the double-action mechanism allows the operator to gently aerate the hay by kicking under the back. The ' over the top ' action really turns the hay completely or kicks over the top according to the speed used on the reel. Further particulars will gladly be supplied by your usual Agent or you can write to us direct.

✱ *Contact your usual dealer without delay – supplies will be limited during the season!*

MAXIMUM MANOEUVRABILITY!

The drawbar can be changed in a matter of minutes to the end towing position for ease of transport through narrow lanes and gateways, the transport width then being 4 ft. 10 ins. only.

SOLE MANUFACTURERS

JONES BALERS LTD

MOLD, NORTH WALES

Sales Department : Broncoed Park Works. Tel : Mold 701
Service & Spare Parts Department : Esmor Works, Rhosesmor, Mold. Tel : Halkyn 363. Grams : Jobalers, Mold

Gather an EXTRA HARVEST NOW! by placing your order AT ONCE for the famous JONES Minor BALER MARK IV. with your usual Dealer.

NOW IS THE TIME to order the World's best baler! JONES BALERS LTD. now offer exceptionally generous out-of-season terms for a limited period only. See your dealer at once, or write to the manufacturers direct.

AVAILABLE AS A
P.T.O. DRIVE MODEL,
OR WITH
DIESEL UNIT.

SAVE up to £51. 0. 0
(NOVEMBER TERMS)

The terms are too good to last very long —
GET REAPING NOW!

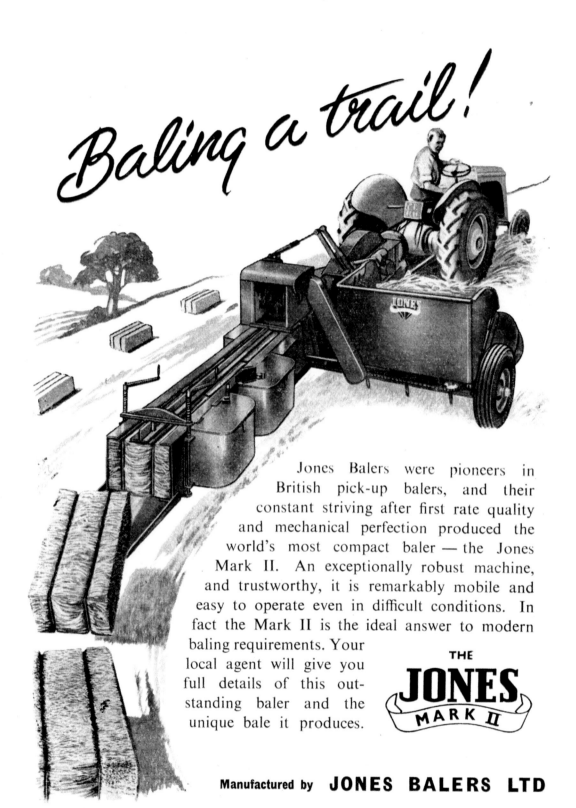

Baling a trail!

Jones Balers were pioneers in British pick-up balers, and their constant striving after first rate quality and mechanical perfection produced the world's most compact baler — the Jones Mark II. An exceptionally robust machine, and trustworthy, it is remarkably mobile and easy to operate even in difficult conditions. In fact the Mark II is the ideal answer to modern baling requirements. Your local agent will give you full details of this outstanding baler and the unique bale it produces.

THE
JONES
MARK II

Manufactured by **JONES BALERS LTD**

RHOSESMOR, Nr. MOLD, NORTH WALES Telephone: Halkyn 363

SOLE MANUFACTURERS OF THE WORLD'S LARGEST RANGE OF BALERS

Japonica Press

Look out for these publications from Japonica Press

THRESHING MACHINES - *Trevor Gregory*

The Threshing Machine was surely the greatest single advance in the mechanization of agriculture. The huge reduction in manpower it produced led to rioting and its unpopularity also slowed down the early development of the steam engine. Because of the lack of literature on the subject this new book aims to treat the subject of threshing as a whole. There is a detailed analysis of threshing machine development, design, and construction plus a survey of its builders. The associated ancillary equipment and how these machines were driven is also looked at.

248 pages Illustrated throughout with detailed diagrams, photographs and images. Hardback, ISBN 978-1-904686-21-7

COMBINES IN CAMERA - *Sue Morgan*

In this book avid combine harvester enthusiast Sue Morgan has formed a chronicle of combine photographs. She has been able to capture some of the older models still at work on camera as a record for future generations, together with information about the companies who made them. Pictures include MH 780s, which were once often seen two or three in a field in the 1960's to the 8-14ft cut 10 tonnes an hour models of the 1970's, to the lone giant 40ft cut harvesters of today with upwards of 80 tonnes an hour capacity working in fields of a hundred hectares or more in size.

160 pages, extensively illustrated in colour with photographs from the author's personal collection. Hardback, ISBN 978-1-904686-20-0

TRACTORS IN BRITAIN – *Stuart Gibbard*

The story of the development of tractors in Britain, from the crude agricultural motors of the 1900's to the latest high-tech computerised machines. Illustrated with outstanding archive and contemporary photographs, the book also looks at tractor factories, dealerships and the life of the tractor driver, to present a complete overview of the history of tractors in this country.

194 pages, 341 illustrations (107 in colour) Hardback, ISBN 978-0-954022-21-1

A WORLD-WIDE GUIDE TO MASSEY FERGUSON 100 AND 1000 TRACTORS 1964-1988 - *John Farnworth*

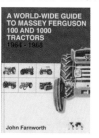

The 100 and 1000 series consists of a range of tractors from about 20-200 hp with all types of chassis combinations – 2 WD, 4 WD, crawlers and articulated. Using Massey Ferguson archive material collected from around the world, John has carefully identified some 250 models and variants, and described each type with specifications and photographs.

310 pages, highly illustrated in black/white & colour. Hardback, ISBN 978-1-904686-05-7

THE MF 500 ERA – THE TRACTOR, THE TIMES AND THEIR IMPLEMENTS - *John Farnworth*

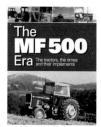

In this book John Farnworth has concentrated on a very short and discrete range of now "Classic" tractors. Relating them to the aspects of manufacture and the countries in which they were sold. In addition he has further developed the overall theme of the MF 500 era presenting an overview of the implements and harvesting machinery which was used with the tractors. Also included are general specifications of the range. The whole MF 500 era is further brought to life in a chapter in which MF employees have recounted their experiences. This book will be of great interest to MF enthusiasts generally, the "Classic" Tractor movement and to anyone with a general interest in farm mechanisation.

272 pages, extensively illustrated throughout in black & white and colour. Hardback, ISBN 978-1-904686-17-0

FERGUSON IMPLEMENTS AND ACCESSORIES - *John Farnworth*

Expanded edition including over 50 more products
The first comprehensive book to be produced on this subject, this book focuses mainly on the wide equipment range produced for the British-made TE tractors but also includes equipment made in the United States for Ford Ferguson and Ferguson TO tractors. There is also reference to implements made for the South African market and a colour section reproducing present-day advertising material from India. Includes technical details from original manufacturers'

literature. A classic for Ferguson enthusiasts!
220 pages, approx. 450 mainly black & white photographs.
Hardback, ISBN 978-1-904686-08-8

THE ROAR OF DUST AND DIESEL – A Story of International Harvester, Doncaster - *Mike Teanby*

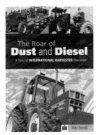

The author describes his first-hand experience of factory life at International Harvester, Doncaster, together with many excellent products built here: Farmall BMD, B450, 885XL and Maxxum, giant industrial PAY-loaders, crawlers, balers, combines, even some of the high horsepower farm tractors imported from Europe and North America. Superbly illustrated with photographs covering every significant machine, model and type built and sold onto British farms.
204 pages, well illustrated throughout in black/white & colour.
Hardback, ISBN 978-1-904686-06-4

DAVID BROWN TRACTORS: A BRITISH LEGEND – *Colin Holwell*

This outstanding book presents a detailed, in-depth history of David Brown Tractors Ltd, and its parent company, David Brown Engineering, from the early connections with Ferguson right through to the red Case 94 series. Each of the famous David Brown lines is described with the aid of many superb colour photographs, some splendid archive material from the company's early days, and reproductions of sales brochures. The book also includes David Brown implements, crawlers and the unconventional 2D, all Meltham-built products.
151 pages, 188 colour & 39 black/white photographs.
Hardback, ISBN 978-1-904686-01-9

HORSEDRAWN FARM IMPLEMENTS – *Edward Hart*

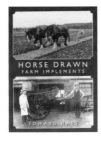

Written by highly regarded countryman and heavy horse enthusiast Edward Hart, this book represents the first in-depth, comprehensive work on horse drawn implements.
Ploughing, cultivating, seeding, harvesting and haymaking implements are all covered, and there are also sections on harnesses and brasses. The many illustrations include some splendid archive material, manufacturer's catalogue illustrations and contemporary photographs. A wealth of information on a subject rarely covered in print.
Foreword by Clarissa Dixon Wright.
160 pages; colour & black/white illustrations. Hardback, ISBN 978-1-904686-03-3

NUFFIELD, LEYLAND & MARSHALL 1948-85 - *Michael D J Irwin*

A history of Nuffield, Leyland & Marshall from 1948 to 1985 in fascinating black & white photographs, with informative text and captions. Also includes specification tables and serial numbers. Excellent value.
66 pages, black & white illustrations.
Softback, ISBN 978-1-904686-11-8

FORDSON NEW MAJOR E1A's 1951-64 – *Allan T Condie*

Covers the development of the New Fordson Major from its inception in 1951 to the end of British Fordson production in 1964 with the New Performance Super Major, plus the Spanish built Ebro variants. A wealth of information in the form of black & white photographs, detailed diagrams, line drawings and technical data tables, including serial numbers.
65 pages, black & white illustrations. Softback, ISBN 978-1-904686-19-4

FORDSON MAJOR 'E27N' 1945-52 – *Allan T Condie*

Detailed text with many black & white photographs, exploded diagrams and line drawings showing each stage in the development of the tractor. Packed with detail, this book represents excellent value for money.
66 pages, black/white illustrations.
Softback, ISBN 978 1 904686 10 1